# THE
# BANKRUPTCY DIARIES

# THE
# BANKRUPTCY DIARIES

## PAUL BRODERICK

REVENGE INK

The author wishes to thank Katie Harnett, Robert Cotter, Deborah Dawkin, Kevin Conroy Scott and Amita Mukerjee

British Library Cataloguing in Publication Data
A catalogue record for this book is available from the British Library

Revenge Ink
Unit 13 Newby Road, Hazel Grove, Stockport Cheshire, SK7 5DA, UK

www.revengeink.com

ISBN 978-0-9565119-3-5

Typeset in Paris by Patrick Lederfain

Printed in the EU by Pulsio Ltd.

*This is a work of fiction and is dedicated to anyone
who ever had a sleepless night caused by debt*

# A Bank Account is for Life

*'Don't wait 'til your tea's gone cold.*
*Apply now and you could have the money in days.'*

Promotional literature from EGG, 2006

Tuesday 5 September, 2000
10.35 a.m. Saltford: Lucy's parents' house.

It arrived in the post this morning. Heard the sound of the mail being forced through the letterbox as I lay beneath the bedclothes fondling my morning glory, the dozy warmth of the sun penetrating the thin cotton sheets. Abandoning my dreamy paradise I threw back the covers and streaked downstairs, swinging weightily from side to side as I descended. There it was, the white envelope nestled between a mangled copy of the *Bath Chronicle* and *The People's Friend*. I tore it open in my excitement. Yep - the one I've been waiting for, 'we are pleased to offer you the position…' I got the job. Woo-hoo! I looked up from the letter and caught sight of myself in the hallway mirror, standing buck naked, my still swollen penis pointing menacingly in the direction of the innocent family portraits on the sideboard. Came over all self-conscious and dashed back upstairs to throw on Lucy's pink dressing gown before returning to pore over the contents. I sat at the breakfast bar in the Webber's kitchen with a mug of milky tea feeling rather pleased with myself as I drank in my first notable success.

First up were the requisite phone calls to Mum and Dad. Their boy is starting his career. Oh they were pleased. My father, a builder, was never convinced about me going to university,

'Get a trade son, y' don't want to be messing about with that education lark, quicker you get yourself out into the real world and start earnin' some money, you'll be on the property ladder in no time. You piss about at university and you'll be four years behind everybody else *and* you'll be up to your neck in debt.'

How many times had I suffered hearing this? He was delighted when I dropped out of my Philosophy course after three amphetamine-addled months, not that he was proud of my record-breaking pill-swallowing feats, rather he was able to railroad me into at least doing a 'vocational' course upon my re-entry to higher education. To be fair to him, he was pleased as punch I'd landed a job and would be putting my 'Town Planning' degree to use although he still struggled to comprehend that a man of 23 was just starting work, 'Y' know I'd been earning for seven years by the time I was your age,' he boasted. Like that was anything to be proud of, although I wasn't getting drawn into that conversation again, 'Things are different nowadays, Dad.'

'Oh, I know, son, I'm just saying that's all.'

My mother was much more supportive of my studies, as she never tired of reminding me or anyone who would listen, that I was the 'first person in the family to go to university', her only son, *at university*. Despite my protestations, my graduation picture, which she had blown up to near life-size proportions, was quickly installed above the fireplace in the living room, where it remains in pride of place like a portrait of a head of state or other dignitary. I can't bear to walk into that room whenever we have guests without dying from embarrassment. The distorted dimensions and looming presence of the golden child dressed in his academic robes, missing only his halo, has been the source of much mockery. As soon as my friend Rick saw the enormous picture bearing down on the room, my fears were confirmed, it was a full five minutes before he could stop howling and wordlessly pointing at the wall. News of my first job sparked another flurry of cosseting from mother:

'Look out for something special in the post over the next few days,' she said, talking to me as if I were still in knee-high shorts, 'Mummy's treat.'

'Mum for the umpteenth time, will you stop…'

'Ha ha, you'll always be my special boy.'

'Mum, I'm 23 years old. I've got a girlfriend, a degree *and* a job, will you please…'

'Oh dear, I've got to go, I need a number two.'

Click!

**11.30 a.m.** Just polished off a celebratory fry-up. Got the place stinking like a greasy spoon. Hope Lucy's mum doesn't notice my raid on the fridge. Pat was all too happy for me to stay here while I looked for a job and waited for the lads to sort out a place in Bristol. Lucy's father Roger, an ex-pilot and one for traditional values, took a little convincing. He was none too keen on the prospect of his virginal princess sleeping with her new boyfriend under his roof. We've only been seeing each other for three months but the mother/daughter combination can be a persuasive one. At least now he can tell his pals at the golf club that the resident freeloader who's fucking his daughter and eating his food has found himself a job. I'll drink to that. Wonder if they'll notice if I pinch a beer?

Don't start work for another week so until then I'm sunbathing in the garden while this decent hard-working family are busy doing the nine to five. Feel a bit isolated out here in sleepy Saltford but can't be arsed to use the village bus service. Low on reading material too, it's a choice between Harry Mincer and the Chamber of Faggots or Lucy's copy of *Heat* magazine with all the latest *Big Brother* gossip. There's books in the lounge but only the kind you see in the pages of the Sunday magazines, purely for decoration. There's an entire row dedicated to the complete works of Charles Dickens. In pristine hardback. Neh well, it's too hot to read anyway. Slightly paranoid about my weed smoke wafting across the Drinkwaters' garden next door. They're probably indoors right now, penning an angry letter to their local councillor about the influx of drug barons and lack of community policing.

**2.45 p.m.** Think I've been in the sun too long, looking a bit lobster-like. Passed out on the sun-lounger after smoking half a joint and I'm feeling a little sore. Just read the letter again – thirteen measly grand a year. What the fuck? Four years study, a degree to my name and I'm earning less than the postman. Thankfully my father didn't rub it in when I told him. Ah well, prosperity is still a distant dream. It won't be long before I'm looking back on these days from the head of the boardroom, people hanging on my every word, in awe of my wisdom as I effortlessly solve the problem that's had them scratching their heads for weeks. I'm destined for the good life, I can feel it. Jetting around the world on important business and exotic holidays, Dad'll have to visit me on my yacht in the Mediterranean, 'you've done all right here, son, really you have. Never thought I'd see the day but I have to hand it to you.' Have to make sure I graft away, climb the ladder as quickly as possible.

Well this is it, no more dossing around, time to grow up. Me with a real job – me – a job! So I'm only a Development Control Officer but everybody has to start somewhere. Who knows what doors it'll open? Wonder what the office will be like? Hope there's some decent talent knocking about.

**6.00 p.m.** Everyone's home and delighted with the news. Big smacker from Lucy – MUH! 'well done babes, I'm proud of you'. Even Roger cracked a smile and I could sense his relief as he offered his congratulations. Pat was much less reserved and quickly set about preparing a celebratory dinner, roping a begrudging Roger into peeling a mountain of veg.

**8.00 p.m.** Sister just called. Thought she was ringing to congratulate me on the new job. 'Who are you voting for this week? I hate Mel, she's *such* a bitch, Craig has to win, he's sooooo lovely.' It's the penultimate eviction week on *Big Brother* and things are hotting up. 'Did Mum tell you that your big brother has a job?' I asked.

'Yeah, well done, shit, Eastenders is on.'

Click!

### Thursday 7 September, 2000

**10.45 a.m. Saltford.** More good tidings in the post. Took delivery of a new job starter pack courtesy of mother: one brand new pair of Clarks complete with a tube of 'instant wax shine' (roll-on) shoe polish and the obligatory congratulation card. The image on the front is of a young whippersnapper in a meeting, clutching a fluffy brown bear above a message: 'James didn't need good luck cards for his new job… not with his teddy by his side.'

### Saturday 9 September, 2000

**4.45 p.m. Bath City Centre: Café Nero.** Spent my afternoon battling the weekend hordes in search of new work clobber. An essential exercise – had to borrow one of Lucy's dad's suits for the interview, complete with distinctly unfashionable velvet elbow patches.

If shopping is officially the number one leisure activity in Britain, then I certainly made my contribution to this statistic. Surprised my card didn't get rejected: two new suits, five shirts, three ties, shoes and even a set of shiny cufflinks. Yes, new shoes. The Clarks have been deposited at the charity shop. Want to look the part on the first day, don't want to be mistaken for a sixth-former on work experience.

**6.15 p.m.** Rock 'n' roll. Had a trying-on session in front of the mirror to the crackle of *LA Woman* on the stereo – the soundtrack to my youth. When I was growing up I wanted to be Jim Morrison. I was obsessed with *The Doors* and their dark lyrics, but what really captured my teenage imagination and thirst for excitement were the tales of Jim's wild excesses. I devoured the biographies and knew all the stories. Jim lived a short but beautiful existence, he resided on the edge, always pushing the boundaries.

Imitation is a common feature of adolescence, we're not yet sure of who we are, so we try other people on for size. Invariably they don't fit. In homage to my hero I grew my hair unsuitably long, wore tight black denims and an open denim shirt over a plain white T-shirt and shades. Instead of looking like a lithe front man prowling across the stage, I resembled a scrawny teenager dressed in hand-me-downs and afflicted by a light allergy.

Of course I had my critics – growing up in Britain, one gets used to being heckled from passing cars for daring to look even slightly different. No matter, I took my emulation seriously and put it down to the close-minded attitudes of a small town. Although my mother was horrified the day I announced that I wanted a pair of leather trousers for my sixteenth birthday and did everything in her power to dissuade me. She, quite correctly, thought I'd attract the wrong sort of attention, not from the passing traffic but from more sinister quarters. Our local park, and more specifically the public toilets, had a certain reputation.

At first it was harmless, but as I got a bit older, my fixation didn't stop at fashion. Full of the anticipation of adolescence, at what great adventures and pleasures life would bring, I thought that if I followed Jim's road I'd get to the heart of it. An advocate of the short intense life at 17, I even told my father I didn't want to live past 30 as there was no point. I'm sure he must've laughed himself silly when he heard that, or at least wondered how he'd spawned such a pretentious poseur.

This was around the time I resolved to set about testing the theory that sensual self-indulgence is the highest good and proper aim of human life. With the single-minded determination of youth and arrogantly ignoring the numerous casualties by the historical roadside, I found out the hard way. As a strung-out 18-year-old, dropped out of university, having barely lasted a term and then working as a night porter, things suddenly didn't seem so enchanting. I didn't have a catalogue of hit records, a cult following or a talent for poetry. I was about three stone underweight and depressed about the future. Crucially, I didn't have the strength of mind, the talent or those other vital ingredients possessed by the unconventional idols of our culture that are essential if one is to stay the course. For the rest of us, the road of excess leads to the night-shift of a businessman's hotel. So I abandoned my vision of living out on the range and decided I'd straighten out, get myself a degree and a career, or at least give myself the option of not having to work *McJobs* the rest of my days.

And look at me now: a reflection of youthful respectability in my Ciro Citterio three piece. Ah well, I like to think you can still lead a good life without taking things to the extreme. Anyway, time to close the door on the past and rejoin the present. Better get changed into my scruffs – promised I'd wash the family fleet as a gesture for the Webber's hospitality.

**Monday 11 September, 2000**
**6.35 p.m. The Detached Des-Res, Saltford.** First day under my belt. Little more than a tiresome procession of meeting and greeting, arranging log-ins and security passes. This was my first glimpse of the office, having been interviewed in the Town Hall. I have to say I was rather disappointed. It wasn't what I'd expected.

I followed the map they'd sent with my joining instructions and it led me to the most tired-looking building in the street, a shabby 1950s monstrosity in a row of elegant Georgian townhouses. Inside was no better, half the people seem to have been there since the official opening. I've never seen so many relics outside of a museum. Oh well, everybody has to start somewhere. I'm prepared to serve my apprenticeship. Still felt like the boy though, swanning around in my new gear. Probably gave a few of the old duffers something to think about. The tank top and sandals brigade better shape up.

Lucy was home waiting to greet the new boy. Mother and daughter kept remarking how smart I looked in my new clothes. I could see they were impressed with the way I'd scrubbed up. Of course ladies, I'm a professional now. They don't need to know the reality of the situation, I'll just phase the clothes out gradually.

**Friday 15 September, 2000**

**3.30 p.m. Bath: Office.** 'Have you voted?' 'Who did you vote for?' Not my sister this time, nor a hastily called general election – it's the *Big Brother* final tonight and the office is buzzing with anticipation. The smart money's on Craig. But his rival Darren has upped his chances by stepping out of the shower, parading his manhood in front of the cameras.

The first week of work has been a breeze, a case of getting my 'feet under the table', in the words of my boss.

**9.30 p.m. Any sitting room, anywhere.** It's the cheeky Liverpudlian builder with the muscles – 'Craig, you have won *Big Brother*.'

Pat and Lucy have been completely hoodwinked by his pledge to donate all of his prize money to charity, refusing to share in my cynicism: 'of course he's giving it away, he knows he'll make ten times that amount on the back of it'.

**Monday 1 October, 2000**

**2.35 p.m. Office.** Bah! Just took a call from the bank. Had no choice but to accept an appointment to discuss repayment of student debts. Boy's got a job – bank wants a cut.

Had been ignoring them in the hope they might forget about me – fat chance.

**Thursday 5 October, 2000**

**2.15 p.m. Work.** Spoke to Pete and Jez at lunchtime. They've finally sorted out a place for us. It's taken them long enough. Been feeling like an intruder at the pilot's lodge, hadn't planned on staying so long. You know what they say about guests and fish, well I'm a rotting king prawn sewn into the lining of the curtains. It's time to ship out. The Webbers have been very good to me but living with your girlfriend and her parents in the fledgling weeks of a new relationship is never ideal. Certainly can't consider chucking her for the foreseeable.

Glad to be moving back with the boys. Lucy's video library consists solely of chick-flicks – mostly starring a typecast Hugh Grant as a bumbling love interest – and every available series of *Friends*. Have developed 'Friends Fatigue' from being forced to watch at least three episodes a night. 'So no one told you life was gonna be this way, CLAP-CLAP-CLAP-CLAP…'

### Monday 9 October, 2000
**10.15 a.m. Work.** First payday today – a *reality cheque*. 'No way, I can't believe how many peanuts they've stuffed into this envelope,' I cried on opening my first payslip, my boss, Geoff, looking at me scornfully upon hearing my *bon mot*. Need to learn to keep my mouth shut. At least Heidi the admin girl found it funny. I've already caught her making eyes at me. Although I do have some morals, the girl's straight out of school – it wouldn't be right. Unbelievably, she's the only female in here worth a look, just one out of an entire department! Am already thinking I should've tried for a job in advertising.

### Thursday 12 October, 2000
**11.30 a.m. Work.** I've barely been here a minute and Pete's nearly got me fired. The twat forwarded a video clip to my work account – a drunk man at a festival, flopping his tadger out and pissing all over the row in front – WITH SOUND! Managed to close it down before anyone could see what it was. Bell-end.

**6.30 p.m. Home.** Returned the favour and sent a clip of a woman firing ping-pong balls from her clacker to Pete's work address. That'll teach him.

### Saturday 14 October, 2000

**4.45 p.m. Bristol: Our new bachelor pad.** Moved house today, the boys are back together and it's a weekend-long party. If my mother had her way I'd be back in Northampton stripping wallpaper, so moving provided me with a convenient excuse to escape her latest redecorating exercise. This time it's a minimalist makeover of the entire downstairs. An approach that's in vogue right now according to the estate agent she had round for the valuation: 'It's what prospective buyers are looking for,' she explained knowledgeably, 'people like a blank canvas to make it easier to impose their own tastes.' No doubt quoting her representative verbatim.

Any excuse. Her passion for interior design borders on a fetish. As soon as she finishes one room she's thinking what to do with the next. And when there's nothing left to change on the inside she's having plans drawn up for a new extension or getting quotes for landscaping the garden, it never stops. I have my own theories on this perpetual improvement and modernising: an acute sense of working class pride, being overly concerned with how one is perceived and feeling judged on the neatness and appearance of one's home. Failing that, it's just a bored woman's response to the existentialist dictum: *something must happen, anything must happen*. It gives her something to do.

I'm fairly indifferent to it these days, but what really used to get me, back when we were kids, was how she'd rule the finances with despotic fervour, screaming at us for wasting food or electricity, and then out of nowhere the Gods of Hire Purchase would come careering towards our door on their wheeled Bedford chariot to bestow a new three-piece suite upon us. Sure enough, she eventually got herself into a bit of bother, over-extended herself and had to endure a period of enforced parsimony at the bank's behest. At least we had nice chairs to sit in.

Which is more than I can say for the shit-hole we've just taken possession of. Hardly the upwardly mobile professional pad I was expecting. It was all we could afford. The sofas smell of death and are covered in decades of dog hair, and we're sure somebody must've died in one of the chairs. If you punch them, clouds of dust and dead skin spew into the air. The boys managed to knock the landlord down on the rent and he's recovered some of his losses by neglecting to have the place cleaned. Walked in to bacon rind welded to the grill pan and a nice thick covering of orange urea all over the shower panels – no different to all the other student hovels we've lived in. The coveted first pay cheque has been quickly devoured by rent, deposit and agency fees. What my father calls 'the real world'.

### Monday 16 October, 2000
**1.40 p.m. Office.** Summoned to the bank at lunchtime to be served another slice of reality pie. Walked in clutching my budget plan and vain hopes of emerging relatively unscathed. Their representative was already waiting for me when I arrived and he promptly escorted me to a windowless back office where it was straight down to business. The branch supervisor (according to his badge) began tapping my details into his computer and scrutinising my figures, mutely glancing from one to the other as I sat patiently waiting for his verdict.

And then he began: 'So, Mr Livingson, I see that you have a significant overdraft which considerably exceeds the agreed limit on your account. We need to look at your finances now that you're earning, and work out a payment plan.'

He pulled out his calculator and began tapping away, scribbling secret sums as I started to grow restless waiting for him to say something more. It was clear that interrupting him would only prolong the procedure, so the room remained uncomfortably silent until he put down his pen and began tapping on his keyboard, and without looking away from the screen announced that a 'graduate loan' would be the appropriate solution.

'Your monthly payment will be £150 and will be deducted from your account the day after your salary is received,' he said coldly, finally looking me in the eye as he added, 'which I'm sure will leave you sufficient funds for living expenses', handing me back the budget plan complete with his revisions.

'But that only leaves me £50 a week. I can't live on that!' I spluttered, incredulous at the injustice being meted out.

'Well I don't have £50 a week to spend,' came the stony response from the unsympathetic suit behind the desk. *That's because you're a joyless dork who saved all his pocket money from the age of five to put a deposit on a house the day you left school you sad muppet*, I fumed wordlessly in my head. I was dumbstruck. Of all the things to say.

It was abundantly clear I had little choice in the matter. Sensing the futility of protest, I sat quietly seething and waited for him to prepare the paperwork, refusing to talk trifles with the heartless bastard who'd just burst my new job balloon and left me utterly deflated. 'But I don't have £50 a week,' I mimicked in my head. Sanctimonious prick. I wanted to grab him by the tie and drag him across the desk: 'Now you listen to me you little twat. I don't care what…' Ultra-violent fantasies flashed through my mind.

The printer beside the desk started chugging out documents which the supervisor arranged methodically on the table. As he stood, I thought how shabby he looked, dressed in an ill-fitting slate suit that hung loosely on his thin frame. 'C&A Man' had condemned me to pauperdom. This guy looks like the kind of man who irons his underpants and considers a night in with a movie and a bumper box of Maltesers to be letting his hair down, I sneered to myself. Perhaps a model railway enthusiast that still lived with his mum?

My character assassination was abruptly halted as he motioned for me to sign the papers. As I scribbled my mark to certify my agreement to the terms, he bizarrely gave me a bit of sales patter: 'Under our terms, the interest rate on a Graduate Loan is a special rate that is fixed for the lifetime of the loan', as if this was something to be thankful for. *Oh I am lucky, the interest rate on the loan I never wanted compares favourably to other commercial rates available, I really don't know how to thank you.*

**3.45 p.m. Office.** That's me well and truly shafted thanks to that dreary little wank-stain at the bank. Condemned to 37 hours a week behind a desk with only a pocketful of loose change to show for it. Turn back the clock. Only weeks ago

I was dossing around in Europe without a job. Days spent kicking a ball about in the sun, high on weed. Evenings sitting outside the cafés working the novelty of the English accent on those lovely Dutch girls. Ah, if I close my eyes for a minute… This new chapter has not begun well.

So this is why the banks are so willing to lend jobless students pots of cash: once you drop off the conveyor belt into the world of work they've already got you by the balls and £50 worth of free record tokens suddenly starts to look very costly.

# Local Government Man

*'Graduates who leave university with debt now owe
on average £12,363.'*

Natwest 'Student Money Matters' press release, 2007

## Saturday 11 November, 2000

**6.30 p.m. Bristol: Home.** The new place has fleas. We're completely infested. Tried to get hold of the landlord but according to his secretary he's on holiday, skiing in the Alps. Apparently we'll have to sit tight until he returns as she's 'only minding the shop'. Phoned the Council who quoted us £200 to have the place fumigated.

Can't even escape to the pub. We're all permanently skint. Seems a degree isn't quite the passport to riches it once was. So this weekend's entertainment is limited to watching the football results on Teletext, clutching our bet slips hoping for a big win. Lucy, whose suggestion of going window-shopping was rebuffed in favour of a day at home with the fleas, sits stewing behind a copy of *Cosmo*, penning her answers to this month's quiz: 'Is He Right for You? Is your guy more Fred Flintstone than New Man?' Questions, questions, questions...

## Thursday 14 December, 2000

**10.21 a.m. Bath: Work.** Thinking of asking for a pay rise. Maybe then I'll be able to afford a rail-pass. Bunking the train was proving to be an effective cost-saver until this morning's incident: being hauled out of the lavatory by a militant inspector. Had to suffer a humiliating dressing-down in front of the other passengers as he took my details. As if that wasn't mortifying enough, my shame was compounded when I spotted the cute girl from the sandwich shop standing by the door. That's the last time I go there for lunch.

**9.30 p.m.** Just got off the phone to Big Dave from uni. He's always fancied himself a bit of a player and now the spawny git's gone and landed himself a twenty-grand job in the city at the first time of asking. Felt like a total failure when I had to tell him about my thirteen tiddlywinks-a-year Council role. Already dreading the first reunion. Although, when it comes to peer group positioning, none of us can touch Andy. He's gone straight into the big league with his investment banking role – Morgan Stanley, no less. Dave told me he met him for lunch in Canary Wharf, sat out on the benches at the foot of that enormous skyscraper you always see on the business news. He explained our friend's new regime of the 5 a.m. alarm call after late nights spent slamming shots onto the bar, with an air of malignant pleasure. In the shadow of a friend's success we derive comfort in hearing of their suffering. According to Andy, they're testing him by being deliberately demanding, just to see if he can handle it.

But at least he knew what he wanted to do. I remember when he was going through the 'milk round', applying for jobs with all these prestigious global corporations before his finals. The rest of us would sit thumbing through the brochures that dropped through the door for amusement, our mockery masking the feeling that we should perhaps be taking life a little more seriously. The one I remember best was from Citigroup, I think it was them. It had all these cheesy biogs of young whiz-kids set underneath a half-page black and white photo, shots of them at their desks with phones clamped to their ears or standing in a pose looking purposefully across the trading floor. Maybe next year's crop of hungry graduates will find our Andy featured in their glossy? I'd love to see that. Although I doubt he's suitable, he might put people off. In every group photo we've got, he stands out like an inconsistent intruder. Whether it's the intensity of his stare or his plump features and oily skin, he's the first one your eyes are drawn to. He's got a face like a fiendish cherub.

After the job-hunting, the devil's child spent his summer working his way through piles of banking and finance books, great thick doorstops, all of them. When your new employer gives you a six-grand golden handshake before you've even done a day's work, they expect a little commitment in return.

**Friday 15 December, 2000**
**12.30 p.m. Bath: Work.** After yesterday's degradation on the train, driven by desperation, I plucked up the courage to visit the head honcho's office to broach the subject of a pay hike. Bad move. Considering Colin Greyweather's reaction I might as well've asked him if I could fuck his wife. The irritated look he shot me when I rapped on his door was a clear signal to do an about turn.

'Yes, what is it?' he snapped as I gingerly made my way into his room to stand in front of his desk like a schoolboy before the headmaster. He didn't offer me a seat. I started to outline my predicament, fumbling for the right words, intimidated by his abrasive manner and unnerving gaze that remained fixed on me as I struggled to table a coherent request. I'm sure I sounded slightly retarded.

As I continued to blather with Greyweather growing ever more impatient, I was momentarily distracted by a photo on the shelf above his head: a comical wedding picture of the stocky Colin arm-in-arm with a stern looking giantess who had a least a foot on him. It looked like one of those seaside souvenirs where holidaymakers are photographed sticking their heads through holes in life-size cartoons. I became aware that I'd stopped talking.

'I haven't got all day,' snarled Greyweather, clearly annoyed by my dithering. Jolted, I came straight out with it: 'I was wondering if there was any way you could raise my salary?'

His expression changed instantly, crimson blotches of anger appearing on the side of his pale face. He placed his hands on the desk and leant forward as if to stand. I thought he was about to go for me.

'You've been here five minutes and you're already asking me for a pay rise?' he stammered, a droplet of spittle catching in his thick military style *'tache*. At that point it felt as though the room had shrunk to a fraction of its size and our faces were only inches apart. I opened my mouth to try and backtrack but nothing came out.

'Well then,' he exclaimed sharply, 'if you've the audacity to stroll into my office like this Mr Big-shot, *please* do tell me what it is you've done to merit such an award?' His voice was shaking with rage.

Reeling from the ferocity of his response, I could only mumble something feeble about there 'being no harm in asking' before bolting out the door to escape his wrath. Back at my desk it took me a full fifteen minutes to regain my composure. Plan to keep my head firmly below the parapet for the foreseeable.

**1.30 p.m.** Now the whole world is against me. Received a ticking-off from my team leader, Geoff. He was piqued to learn that I'd 'marched' into Greyweather's office without consulting him first. 'There's a way of going about things,' he said disapprovingly, handing me a copy of the *Local Government Pay Scale Index*, courtesy of the man at the top. Really shouldn't have bothered getting out of bed this morning.

**2.00 p.m.** Article on MSN: 'Ten Ways to Get Ahead at Work'. Oh how I laughed.

**2.15 p.m.** Thinking of submitting my own piece to MSN: 'Beware the grey men of the world – why a dole application could be better than a job application'.

**Tuesday 19 December, 2000**
**11.45 a.m. Office.** It's the little big man on a power trip. Greyweather's refusing to make eye contact with me in the corridor. Initially thought I was being paranoid but I've passed him several times since our showdown and he's looked right through me. Petty bastard.

**2.30 p.m.** Rang payroll to cancel my pension subscription. It's all I could think to do. Can't afford to be wasting precious resources on a bloody retirement fund of all things. Need all the money I can get.

**3.30 p.m.** That man has become my nemesis. Walked into the gents to relieve myself only to rub shoulders with Colonel Colin at the cramped two-man trough. Had to endure a mute standoff with him in full thundering flow while I pushed and strained against knob constipation, trying desperately to overcome my mental blockage. Almost started humming a tune to disguise my lack of stream. We both knew I had stage fright and wouldn't pass a drop until he'd left the room. Awful. Truly awful.

**Friday 22 December, 2000**
**2.35 p.m. Office. Messages (1).** The dirty dog. Went out for a festive pint with Justin at lunch. A fellow graduate hired at the same time as me. He spent the whole hour giving me the low-down on his internet dating exploits, how he spends the work day chatting to girls he then meets for casual 'encounters'. For someone who takes an inordinate interest in their appearance, those dating sites provide the perfect platform for his vanity.

His hair is a work of art: a constantly evolving display of über-trendy styles. I'm always ribbing him that he spends more time in the bathroom than all the women I know, but he seems to take a perverse pride in this. That man could fall in love with his own reflection, in fact he'd make an ideal *Big Brother* contestant. I even overheard him telling Heidi he was thinking of applying next year. 'Day twenty-three in the Big Brothah Howse and Justin has bin lookin' in the mirra' for sevun ow-as.'

He's also a marketing man's wet dream: all his clothes are designer labels. Only this morning he was trying to show me his new Tommy Hilfiger briefs. 'Twenty-five quid they set me back,' he boasted, lifting his shirt to show me the waistband with the manufacturer's motif emblazoned across the elastic. 'What, for one pair of pants?' I bawled. It's been puzzling me for a while now, how we can both be on the same salary with him able to dress like a catwalk model while Oxfam is barely within my price range. When I pressed him on it, he opened his wallet to show me his bright green EGG credit card, 'Six grand limit,' he said mischievously, 'bloody lethal though.'

**Thursday 28 December, 2000**
**11.45 a.m. Northampton.** A double celebration last night: Rick's housewarming party and his surprise coronation as salesman of the year. Having taken the radical decision to quit university after only one week, deciding that he didn't want to be racking up debts when he could be out there earning and building his empire, he set himself the challenge of being well ahead of his mates by the time they hit the work trail. And he's sure as hell succeeded.

'You're a regular Richard Branson,' I heckled, when he announced his award to the room after we'd all devoured the lavish buffet his girlfriend Abby had painstakingly prepared. He didn't mind the comment at all, laughing along with the rest of us, happy to accept a gentle ribbing. Not only had he just bought his first house, but in a matter of four years he'd managed to out-perform all his senior colleagues to scoop up the top accolade. They must seriously hate him.

'I bet they'd have disqualified you if they found out how much puff you smoked,' joked his lodger, Austen, handing Rick a reefer. 'Did you win anything else aside from that bloody plaque?'

On the wall next to the food table was a newly-hung brass plaque, commemorating his success. The company logo had been engraved at the top of the tablet, above a banner that read: 'ADS FINANCIAL SERVICES – SALESMAN OF THE YEAR 2000 – RICKY BRIGHT'. Beneath the banner was a photo of Rick in his tuxedo, receiving a cut-glass decanter from his boss.

'Look at the protégé and his mentor,' I said, taking my opportunity to return the mockery he'd dealt me over my graduation memento.

'Hardy, ha, have your jokes. If you must know I'm off to Paris next week, all expenses paid.'

Austen and I looked at each other and then at Rick.

'Fair play,' I said, my tease having lost a little of its effect after that comeback.

All night long I couldn't take my eyes off the photo: Rick, tall and skeletal, his pale, unhealthy face contrasting starkly with the deep black of the over-sized suit. Even at 23, he already looked like a seasoned businessman. And now he was beginning to enjoy the trappings. He didn't say as much, but from the quiet look of contentment that he wore all evening, Rick clearly felt vindicated over his years spent knocking on doors selling insurance, while his pals sat around getting stoned and playing Scrabble.

The evening descended into disgraceful drunkenness. Rick was clearly in a celebratory mood and his happiness rubbed off on the rest of us. He even allowed us to graffiti the spare room, since he would be decorating the place in the New Year. As dawn broke, we all painted profanities about one another on the walls, our stomachs hurting from laughing so hard.

### Saturday 30 December, 2000

**5.15 p.m. Milton Keynes.** Had to put in an appearance at the old man's before escaping back to Bristol for New Year high jinks. Sat slumped in his chair, recovering from the effects of another Christmas dinner, Dad jerked awake on hearing word of Rick's accomplishments. And I thought the old bugger wasn't listening.

'Well you're playing catch-up, I've told you that before,' he said, bolting upright in his seat. 'This should be your motivation boy. When you see your friends getting ahead of you like that.'

'It's not a race,' I cried incredulously, appalled at his twisted take on life.

'I told you university was…' he stopped mid-sentence and caught himself before changing his line, 'I haven't seen Rick for years,' he said longingly, 'maybe you should invite him over?'

'Well he's a busy man these days but I could have a statue made of him if you want…'

'Cheeky bugger, always ready with a smart answer. You won't

find things so funny when you're living out your days on a Council estate.'

I rolled my eyes at his ludicrous exaggeration.

'Are you moving house?' I said, having spotted a welcome diversion in the form of an estate agent's property spec laying on top of his *Daily Mail*.

'Ah no, not really, me and Jan just like being a bit nosey when we've a few days off and a bit of time to kill. We just find it interesting looking round people's houses.'

'You mean you go on viewings just to snoop around?' I shrieked, eager to seize on this gem of a confession.

He laughed a little awkwardly, fidgeting in his chair. Now it was him on the back foot. Gleefully, I went in for the kill.

'Who do you think you are, Lloyd fucking Grossman? You pair of perverts, that's voyeurism that is. Those poor people, thinking you want to buy their house and all you want to do is peek in their washing basket. That's sick.'

I'd really flustered him. He picked up his paper, flapping it noisily, and opening it out wide in a deliberate display so I could no longer see his face, mumbled something incomprehensible behind the pages. I sat chuckling quietly as his wife, Jan, entered the room to offer us dessert.

**Monday 8 January, 2001**
**09.52 a.m. Office.** Back to work after the Christmas break with a heavy dose of the New Year blues. Same tedious tale: I'm writing my reports, hitting my targets, I even had a good appraisal. I'm just not being rewarded for my exertions. Seems I'd wrongly assumed the working life would afford a certain standard of living, but this is bullshit. Thought I'd have a whole new wardrobe by now, be eating

out every weekend, living it up. And as for going on a holiday – bah! I'll be lucky if I get a day out in Clacton. Hardly seems worth it. Not much to do but plod away here until a better opportunity arises elsewhere. Oh, I got the New Year blues…

**1.30 p.m. Jailbird_69.** Justin brightens my day. He could see I was looking a bit glum and in need of a lift, so he took me out to lunch for the latest instalment of 'the life of a chatroom stud'. He's only spent Christmas servicing a woman whose husband's in prison.

The human clotheshorse was also sporting a brand new Paul Smith shirt, very loud and expensive. A Christmas treat to himself, as he put it when I commented on his attire. I put his obsession with image down to a case of 'little man syndrome'. With his blonde locks and blue eyes he's sure been blessed with the looks, but cruelly short-changed in the height department.

**3.30 p.m.** Myself and Justin have begun collecting office clichés for amusement. The people in here willingly throw them about and with no sense of irony. If they're not 'singing from the same hymn sheet' then they're suggesting 'we run it up the flagpole to see if anyone salutes it'. You look on in disbelief, waiting for them to follow it with a knowing laugh, some form of acknowledgement, but nothing. You don't have to be mad to work here but you do need to be fluent in *moron*.

We've drawn up a checklist of them that we use to log a running tally next to people's names. Each time we hear one being used, we shoot each other a gleeful look as the culprit scores a point. We're planning a secret award for the winner. Geoff's out in front at the moment. After lunch I heard him on the phone, telling someone who was chasing him on something, that they'd 'be the first cab out the rank'.

### Monday 15 January, 2001
**11.00 a.m.** Payday today. The cancelling of the pension has yielded me a poxy £30 extra in my take-home, which is roughly an increase of about a pound a day.

### Friday 19 January, 2001
**10.45 a.m. Work.** Hit the 'snooze' button countless times this morning before mustering the mental strength to throw myself out of bed. At five-minute intervals the sharp, rapid bleep would shock me awake, sending a wave of torment through my body. It was still dark outside and my room was freezing. I'd open my eyes and see the bright red numbers on the clock display and pray they were wrong. When I finally did rise, shivering and chattering, I got myself ready in a foul temper, wondering which sadistic bastard it was who decreed that the week should be so weighted in favour of work. Surely a three-day weekend is more befitting the nature of man?

### Friday 2 February, 2001
**3.30 p.m.** Competition closed – Justin's counted up the cliché scores for the last month and it was no shock to see Geoff come out on top. Although Clive ran him close with his insistence on 'chucking it in the pond to see if it swims'. We're prepared for the inevitable gags on Monday when Geoff finds the bottle of 'Old Chestnut' ale we've planted in his drawer.

## Sunday 11 March, 2001

**10.30 a.m. Saltford.** I should never have agreed to it. Having spent my adolescence in an all-female household being bombarded with boy band 'culture' by my mother and sister, I thought I'd finally escaped the choreographed capers of the manufactured puppets. But it was Lucy's birthday and Robbie 'Take That' Williams just happens to be her favourite. I felt I had little choice.

As I boarded the chartered coach that had been booked to ferry the Bristol branch of the Robbie Williams fan club to the Birmingham NEC, I was confronted with the horrifying sight of rows of excitable mothers and daughters, mingled with a clutch of equally cheerful fathers and boyfriends. I scolded myself for being such a walkover as I slipped into my seat.

I was too disgusted with myself to play the agreeable partner and pushed myself up against the window. Lucy could sense my unease and attacked me, 'I wouldn't have brought you if I knew you'd be like this,' she said huffily. She turned to engage with her friends and I took the opportunity to bury myself in my Jack Kerouac novel.

Halfway along the M5, with the sound of Robbie's greatest hits on the bus stereo, my phone rang.

'Alright mate, what you up to today? We're in the pub at the moment, remember I'm DJ'ing tonight at that party?' It was Pete calling.

'Can't mate, out with Lucy today.'

'Where are you?'

I hesitated. I couldn't bring myself to tell him. Lucy was looking at me frowning.

'On a bus,' I mumbled.

'Where to?'

I was silent for a moment as I tried to think of a lie.

'Come on, stop pissing about, where are ya?'

'Oh fuck it,' I hissed seething, 'I'm going to see Robbie fucking Williams at the fucking NEC,' I snarled, unable to contain my displeasure. Lucy dug me sharply in the ribs.

'Fuck off,' he said laughing. 'No, seriously, where are you?'

'I'm not lying,' I said dejectedly, preparing to take the inevitable abuse. 'It's Lucy's birthday, she had tickets. I had no choice.' Caught between ridicule and the reproach of my girlfriend, I elected to try and save face. I yelped as Lucy attacked me again, pinching me hard in the side.

'HA HA HA!' he roared down the phone. 'That's the best thing I've heard in ages, Oi lads, guess where...'

I sank low in my seat as I listened to him relay the scandal to the pub. A drunken chorus of 'Rock DJ' sounded down the phone. I hung up bitterly, conscious of the implications of this indiscretion. As soon as I'd finished, Lucy started in on me again. I felt bad. I didn't mean to spoil her day, but I couldn't suppress my true feelings.

Things failed to improve. Never have I endured a more uncomfortable evening. There's only so many times one can feign the need for a piss. I felt shell-shocked as the music blared around the vast auditorium and the rows of adoring fans bopped and boogied to hit after hit. As I looked around the arena like a trapped rat desperate to find an escape tunnel, I was sickened by the sight of so many grown men dancing energetically alongside their teenage daughters. I'd taken my place amongst the 'comfortable men' of the world. By the end, I was completely destroyed. I'd surrendered my identity and found myself waving goodbye to my dignity by joining in the collective arm-swaying to 'Angels' during the encore, in the hope of a peaceful journey home.

**7.30 p.m. Bristol.** As I turned my key in the door I could hear them sniggering. Walked into the lounge to be greeted with a wailing rendition of 'Angels' from a drunken Pete and Jez, arms aloft swaying in unison. Pricks.

### Wednesday 14 March, 2001

**8.00 p.m. Home.** Lucy's been off with me since the weekend. Understandable really, I did behave rather badly. But I couldn't help my reaction – surely a sign our relationship is founded on difference. Well-mannered and cultivated as she is, part of the initial attraction was that wooing Lucy represented a bit of a challenge. While we were not exactly Mellors and Lady Chatterley, I liked the idea of being with someone from a different background. And it kind of works, well, sometimes. Like when I'm deliberately bawdy or crude and she plays all huffy and exasperated, tutting or rolling her eyes, sometimes standing there with her hands on her hips looking piqued. It's a bit of game, a role-play, with me pushing it further until I see her struggling to suppress a smile. But recently, like so many rituals, the act has become a little tired.

Looking a little deeper into it, I can see that I allowed myself to be misled by those early courtship exchanges. I was impressed that she spoke French and had worked in France for a year. Cultured and courageous – a definite turn-on. But that would now appear to be little more than a box ticked, an experience belonging to the past as she looks to settle into a regular life. The envious tone with which she speaks of her friends' 'more advanced' relationships certainly hasn't escaped me.

**8.30 p.m.** It's stupid really, but in my head I've got this rather idealised image of my older self. I'm looking way into the future, well after the adventures have played out. I picture me and my future partner living together in a battered old townhouse. The place is lined with sagging and bowed bookshelves and is full of general clutter like old globes and maps. The rooms are filled with lamps collected from junk shops, the floors covered with dark patterned rugs that don't match anything else. I have myself a study with a big antiquated desk pushed up against a giant sash window overlooking a garden. Me and my unidentified woman spend our days busy with our respective pursuits, both perfectly in tune with one another. I picture us sat there in big chairs, reading in silence, not having to worry whether the other is bored or not. We have long wine-soaked dinners with interesting friends and take holidays in Europe. I suppose it's a kind of romantic bohemian fantasy. A fanciful notion – I'll probably still be hankering after it like a delusional fool when I'm lying on my deathbed.

### Saturday 14 April, 2001

**4.30 p.m. Bristol.** Big Dave's down for the weekend. The three of us fell about when he walked in the door. It was immediately obvious where he's been spending his earnings, the tills of the designer boutiques must have been singing with delight after he'd left the shop.

'You look like a fireman,' said Jez, pointing at Dave's bright yellow Tommy Hilfiger puffa jacket that he was wearing over a red 'Hackett' polo shirt. Jez was right, with his height and build and that colour scheme, Dave really did look like a fireman.

'It's lovely to see you too, Jeremy,' said Dave, slightly dumbstruck at having walked straight into a wall of piss-taking without so much as a 'hello.'

'You must have the whole fucking alphabet on your back!' bellowed Pete, continuing the taunts, referring now to the array of logos adorning Dave's garments.

It was impossible not to laugh at Big Dave's lack of fashion sense, a classic error of associating the cost of an item with style. Even worse than the puffa were his motif-splattered 'Moschino' jeans, possibly the most garish pair of denims ever created. We only left him alone when he threatened to reconsider his intention to shout us dinner with the proceeds of his two-grand bonus.

### Friday 26 May, 2001
**4.00 p.m. Office.** As City boys round off the week in a nightclub watching nubile young women gyrate on a pole, Council workers huddle together in the staff canteen to witness the coronation of a creaking dinosaur. At precisely 3:30 everybody was called to assemble and mark a colleague's 25 years of continuous service at the council. Step forward a very awkward-looking Alan Fox from the deepest recesses of the policy dept. Bit my lip when Justin whispered, 'Do his clothes get an award too?' Harsh but fair.

As a ritual, it was excruciating but compelling theatre. The look-away moment being the presentation by Greyweather of a milestone cheque for £100. Said to Justin during the applause that followed – 'That's four quid for every year that he's pissed away in this shithole' – which caused Geoff, who'd been standing in front of us, to turn around and fix us with a reproachful glare. Honestly though, I've never seen anybody look so uncomfortable at being awarded money.

From: Facilities Management
To: All male staff
Date: 29 May 2001 11:40

SUBJECT: Abuse of Male Toilets

Dear all,

This morning a cleaner tendered her resignation as a result of one of the male toilet cubicles being smeared with faeces. This despicable act took place last Friday evening and is not the first incidence of such vandalism. It is my duty to warn whoever is responsible...

### Monday 29 May, 2001

**11.45 a.m. Office.** The office has been thrown into an uproar by news of a phantom shit-smearer. Everyone's under suspicion. Never has the male workforce paid more attention to the state of their fingernails. Hilarity of the scandal aside, some tortured soul has been driven to commit the ultimate act of self-loathing. On more than one occasion. Both myself and Justin are agreed that someone walked into the bathroom that night, caught sight of themselves in the mirror and the '25 today' badge pinned to their pencil tie and started decorating.

### Friday 20 July, 2001

**10.15 p.m. Office.** Ooh, c'mon, c'mon – show me the money! Saw an advert for another job. After months of enforced frugality I'm ready to bail at the first opportunity. Geoff wasn't shy in expressing his disappointment when I told him I intended to apply. He said he'd expected a degree of loyalty after their 'investment in my development'. Sorry, Geoffrey old chap, money talks. But seriously, the people in here don't understand what it's like. Their generation were given a decent start, back when the government actually gave people a helping hand instead of a direct debit form and an IOU. They were lucky enough to graduate with nothing more than a degree certificate and a few notches on the bedpost, not hamstrung by debt and financial worries.

Telephoned the number immediately, application forms are on their way to me in the post. This could be it, fingers crossed.

# The Loan Ranger

*'In the UK consumers borrow £360 million every day.'*

Credit Action Press Release, March 2007

**Wednesday 19 September, 2001**

**3.15 p.m. Office.** Pop the Champagne corks and wheel out the Vol-au-Vents, just received the call informing me I landed the job I applied for. EIGHTEEN THOUSAND POUNDS! I've served my apprenticeship and I'm about to get paid. Can't wait to tell Greyweather where he can stick his pay scale. Still a bit early to be thinking about yachts and penthouses, but keep moving at this rate and I'll have reached the top of the tree by the time I'm 30. Leaving early to celebrate, I've a date with a few pints at the pub.

**Thursday 20 September, 2001**

**9.15 a.m. Office.** Emailed resignation to Greyweather. Tempted to sign off with: 'I have taken the organisation as far as I can', but thought better of it. There's no place for such humour and I need a reference from the miserable bastard.

**10.30 p.m.** Signed Greyweather's work address up to a few gay porn sites. The thought of him on the phone to IT pleading his innocence…

**Friday 21 September, 2001**

**6.30 p.m. Bristol: Home.** What's wrong with people? Rang my dad to tell him of my latest success and impending rise up the career ladder, to which his instinctive response was not to congratulate but, 'Now son y'wanna seriously think about buying somewhere. You can't afford to miss the boat. I know you probably won't be able to do it on your own but what about your mates, y'could all go in together'.

After a year of fare-dodging and nights in front of the TV, I'm finally about to have a bit of money in my pocket and he wants me to join the mortgage belt.

'I couldn't stand the thought of renting,' he continued, 'renting's a mug's game y'know. I just couldn't bear the thought of it,' repeating himself to ram home the point. 'You know what, the way I see it you may as well take your money out of the bank each month, walk into the street and flush it down the drain, because that's effectively what you're doing when you're renting. The thought of paying somebody else's mortgage for 'em, I couldn't stand it, it'd kill me.'

He was getting carried away and pissing all over my parade in the process. He continued his plea: 'You've got to get yourself on the property ladder as soon as you can.'

I couldn't listen to any more of it. I cut him short: 'Dad, the taxi's here, I've got to go.'

### Saturday 22 September, 2001
**11.30 p.m. Bristol: Home.** Lucy's starting to badger me about moving in together. Following a tiresome trawl around the gleaming concourses of the soulless mall at Cribbs Causeway, she made her move in the Marks and Spencer's Café over a plate of penne in mushroom sauce.

'Babes, I've been thinking. We've been together more than a year now and I need to feel this relationship is progressing.'

Hearing those words immediately set off alarm bells in my head. They smacked of problem-page advice. Sensing trouble, I reached for the pepper grinder and began to apply an unnecessary second covering of spice to my lukewarm plastic meal, focusing intently on the plate in front of me.

Then she hit me with it, 'I think we should move in together.' I nearly choked on my food. I hadn't seen it coming and panicked.

'Erm… okay, I hadn't err… well I've not really thought that far ahead,' I said, avoiding a direct rebuttal and an untimely confrontation. Shit, how was I going to skirt around this one? Pete and Jez were doing a Gloucester Road pub crawl after the match. I could picture them already sitting with their beers.

I mumbled something about a new contract with the lads, trying to say as little as possible. A baby in her high chair next to us began wailing.

'You can't expect to doss around with your mates forever,' she said sharply over the din. 'You have to grow up sometime.' She wasn't going to be fobbed off easily. I rubbed my face nervously, looking around the food hall for help. I was trapped, surrounded by shopping bags and spend-weary families. Luckily the kid next to us had a good set of lungs on her. I made a wincing face and told her we'd talk about it tomorrow.

I blame those bloody magazines. I actually feel sorry for women: 'Is HE committed to YOU? Take our test and find out.' 'Question 4 – Has he refused to cohabit? If YES, deduct twenty points from your score and consider giving him an ultimatum.'

Her friends are no help either, they're all buying houses, getting married or having kids. It makes me shudder. They're not yet 30 and have already abandoned the city for the lifeless Lego-brick suburbs. Christ it's like going to visit my dad. And they're all typical British property bores. Man, I hate it whenever we get invited to their interminable dinner parties, and the conversation inevitably turns to how much their little bolt holes are worth: 'We were so worried that we were buying at the top of the market, but we're so glad we did… This place has already appreciated 20 grand in the last 18 months. Graham thinks we should look at a buy-to-let next year.' It makes me want to scream – YOU'RE 27! GET A FUCKING LIFE!

Things are starting to get uncomfortable. I'm only 24. I haven't done anything yet and already the sirens of suburbia are singing out my name.

### Sunday 14 October, 2001
7.30 p.m. Put in the weekly call to mother and got sucked into a conversation I'd rather not have had. Mothers are always eager to know whether there's any prospect of their darling son's current mate becoming their future wife, it's only natural.

'Jesus, you're as bad as her,' I exclaimed, immediately going on the defensive after hearing my mother utter that dreaded phrase, 'wedding bells'.

'She's been on at me about moving in together. Y'know she's got it all mapped out, and she's already warned me that if I get her pregnant she's keeping it. I'm not ready for all that. She's a lovely girl but I just wanna enjoy myself. And I don't see anything wrong with that,' I explained, coming clean on my private thoughts for the first time.

'Of course not darling, you have to be honest. But if she wants those things and you don't, then don't you think it's a little unfair to keep stringing her along?'

I paused for a moment. I hadn't thought of myself as 'unfair' or stringing anybody along.

She continued: 'If you won't give her what she wants, then you're taking her life away from her and stopping her finding those things with somebody else. That's why I left your father, and look at him now.'

Her frankness was making me unbelievably uncomfortable. I also had to stop her before she launched into the story of their divorce again, the details of which are indelibly imprinted on my brain. I garbled some form of vague agreement and excused myself from the conversation by saying my dinner was ready.

**9.30 p.m.** How is it we can so easily dismiss the opinions of friends but the words of our family can completely floor us? My mother's speech was the voice of womanhood forcing me to confront the consequence of my actions: 'you're taking her life away from her'. It succeeded in making me feel incredibly guilty.

For all my bravado I'm really an emotional coward. I can't bear the thought of inflicting pain on someone. No, I have to wake up to the reality – we're incompatible. Hell, I almost wish Lucy wasn't such a nice girl, then I'd have no qualms about dumping her.

### Monday 15 October, 2001
**7.00 p.m. Home.** Letter confirming start date for new job. Only a couple more weeks before this pauper becomes a player.

### Thursday 18 October, 2001
**11.50 p.m. Home.** Lucy's been in London all week on a training course. Grateful for the headspace. Am steeling myself for our separation showdown, a daunting prospect made worse by Jez in the pub earlier, who helpfully responded to my plans to ditch her by saying, 'well she won't go quietly'. And with that comforting thought in mind it's time for bed.

**Monday 5 November, 2001**

**10.35 a.m. Bristol: Office.** First day in the new job. Still the only person under 30, another grey ceiling blocking my path to success. Plenty of time for that later, in the meantime there's payday to look forward to.

**Saturday 10 November, 2001**

**8.30 p.m. Home.** Ah the relief. Overcame my cowardice and broke up with Lucy this afternoon. Jez was right, she didn't take it well: took me half an hour to vacuum up the glass. Reckon I've had a lucky escape. Been having nightmares filled with screaming babies, manicured lawns and giant boxes of Maltesers. The Kid is back.

**Tuesday 13 November, 2001**

**8.30 p.m. Home.** Had to buy a car for work so I've taken advantage of the Council Car Loan scheme to the tune of £5,000. I suppose in one way the job has just cost me five grand but at least I'm on the road. Time for a spin, taking the boys on a whore tour of the city.

**11.45 p.m.** Got pulled over by the rozzers who thought we were curb-crawling. Try explaining to a policeman that a whore tour doesn't actually involve picking up any hookers. Understandably, the local constabulary were none too amused by a bunch of tossers cruising areas of social deprivation for their own puerile entertainment. Luckily, escaped with nothing more than a stern lecture.

**Sunday 30 December, 2001**

**2.30 p.m. Northampton.** Recovering from Rick's annual celebration. I'd been invited to dinner with him and Abby, along with Austen who's still lodging with them. Only a year after being named 'Salesman of the Year', the Boy Wonder's surpassed all expectations, managing to go one further.

'Youngest person in company history to become Area Manager,' said Rick, with a shameless air of self-satisfaction, as he announced his promotion after the raspberry sorbets had been cleared away.

'Did they make you grow that beard before they gave you the job?' I said, desperate for the chance to get a wisecrack in over his newly acquired facial hair. I'd been saving that one, refusing to comment until the perfect opportunity presented itself.

Austen spat his dessert wine onto the tablecloth.

'He's had to sign the sex offenders' register,' said Austen, after he'd stopped choking on wine and laughing. We both exploded, Rick remaining stony-faced as his achievement was consumed by ridicule. Austen was spot on, he looked like the archetypal paedophile with that bushy beard covering his face like a greasy brush. He's far too wiry to carry it off and with his dark eyes he looked more than a little creepy.

'Ahhh, I think it's lovely,' said Abby, coming to his defence. 'You're right though, it does make him look more mature.'

'Seriously,' said Rick, interjecting and speaking up for himself, 'when you're the youngest in the office by some distance you need to gain respect.' This started us off again, and Austen and I were unable to look at one another, battling to suppress our snickers.

'You peckers can say what you want, but youngest ever Area Manager speaks for itself.' Rick was clearly very chuffed with himself and refused to allow our goading to upset him.

'Hey, look what Rick bought me!' said Abby suddenly holding out her hand and flashing a very expensive looking ring that sparkled in the light. 'He took me to Bond Street last weekend, guess how much?'

'£999.99,' said Austen flippantly.

'No it wasn't that much,' answered Rick. 'I got a bonus and the ring was on offer, down from £800 to £600.'

I thought of what I'd spend 600 quid on, definitely a holiday, no question about it.

'Anyway, there was a reason for splashing out,' continued Rick. 'We also got engaged last week.' And he turned to Abby and kissed her passionately in front of myself and Austen, before we could offer our congratulations.

After Abby had recounted the details of Rick's bended-knee moment, we moved onto coffees.

'When are you going to meet a nice girl? I heard you're single again?' asked Abby, looking at me.

'Oh, I'm alright as I am, I'm happy to enjoy my freedom until the right one comes along,' I said, trying to quash the line of enquiry.

A more candid, but probably inappropriate answer given the occasion, would've been 'somebody who's up for a good time', or 'someone who's not afflicted with the British rush to do everything by the time you hit 30'. No wonder so many people get to middle age, panic and end up making a mess of things trying to recapture their lost youth. Maybe it's a consequence of my upbringing, but I've a theory that the high number of people who experience mid-life crises can be blamed on this premature obsession with maturity.

**Tuesday 12 February, 2002**
**10.30 a.m. Office.** Goddammit! An untimely letter from the Student Loans Company. My higher salary means I'm no longer entitled to deferment. I'd completely forgotten about them. Seven grand's worth of distant memories coming home to roost

in the form of a salary-sapping direct debit. And just as you think you're finally getting somewhere – bah! At every turn, there's someone holding their hand out. Derailed by debt once again.

### Thursday 14 March, 2002
**3.45 p.m. Office.** My remuneration may be better but it's not without its drawbacks.

My job involves knocking on doors, flashing my ID badge and sheepishly announcing, 'I'm from the Council'.

When I was a kid, I wanted to be a journalist. Me and my friend Julian were both computer geeks. We'd sit at his dining room table making homemade magazines, writing our own reviews of the latest video games and diligently designing our layouts. Our 'publications' might not have been commercially successful, but at least we retained our artistic integrity. Quite how one goes from such aspirations and promise to trawling around housing estates assessing the visual virtues of modest house extensions is a twist of fate I'm struggling to come to terms with.

### Thursday 11 April, 2002
**12.25 p.m. Café.** The transformation is complete. As of today, I am a respected professional – a credit-card-carrying professional. Had been under the impression I was *persona non grata* at the bank until all my outstanding debt had been repaid. However, it would seem that my name has been taken off the black list and I've become a valued and sought-after customer. Only popped into the local branch of HSBC to update some of my details, but managed to walk out with a Gold Card winging its way to me in the post.

Having updated my details on her system and preparing myself to leave, thinking this brief bit of business concluded, I nearly fell out of my chair when the customer services representative, who looked disturbingly like my aunty Margaret, suddenly announced: 'Now I notice that you don't currently hold any cards with us Mr Livingson, would you like a credit card? I can do that today for you if you'd like?'

*What the… A credit card, me? Today? Are you sure?* I thought to myself, astonished at this unexpected offer of money.

'I thought I wasn't allowed credit cards?' I stammered, genuinely taken aback as aunty Margaret's doppelganger proceeded to inform me that I had a 'good credit rating' and this was probably 'down to the fact I'd been paying off my bank loan regularly'.

'You can even have a Gold Card if you like,' she said, making the second shocking revelation in the space of two minutes. Straight to Gold! No dilly-dallying with the lower-ranked offerings.

It was too much to take. I tried not to look too excited, lest she withdraw the offer if I came across as too eager to get my hands on the keys to the sweet shop. I was sure she'd misread my history and would soon realise her mistake. I decided to play it cool and affect an air of indifference.

'Well I don't think I really need a credit card,' I said casually, to which she replied: 'Well it'd be nice to know you had it, just in case of an emergency.' Which of course sounded totally logical, even though at that precise moment I couldn't quite think what that emergency could be, or what form it would take.

'Yes, yes, I suppose you're right,' I said in agreement. *I'm going to get a Gold Card, a fucking Gold Card, tra-la-la*, went my mind, whirring with all the possibilities a premier status card would give me. I sat on my hands to quell my excitement as she set about the business of ordering my card.

'Right then, your card will arrive in the post within the next five working days. Is there anything else I can do for you?'

'No, no that'll be all,' I said, trying to sound businesslike. And that was it. I left the bank in a spin, already looking forward to flashing my Gold Card to my mates and whipping it out in public. Ha-Ha! What's in *your* wallet lads?

**2.35 p.m. Office.** Still struggling to comprehend events at the bank earlier this afternoon. That woman was almost falling over herself to bestow Gold status upon me. Feeling quite flattered with my new status as a 'high roller'. Must be doing something right: already on my second job and have now even gained the respect of my bank. Never thought I'd be saying that. God bless the Hong-Kong Shanghai Banking Corporation. Life has just opened up in front of me. I can do anything now. Ha-Ha. HELLO WORLD!

**Monday 15 April, 2002**
**6.45 p.m. Home.** It's here and in double-quick time. My spanking new HSBC Gold Card. Put it straight into my wallet, and have been pissing about, waving it at Pete and Jez. It looks impressive in there, nestled between my gym pass and library cards, the bright yellow symbol of status contrasting nicely with the sophisticated dark-leather card-holder. It looks like I've hit the big time.

'What the fuck are you doing with a Gold Card?' scoffed Jez disapprovingly, as I waved the shiny plastic in his face.

'I'm an upwardly mobile professional, you prick. My bank has faith in me.'

'You dick'ead, it's not *your* money is it. You have to pay it back.'

'I'm well aware of that Jeremy. So what's the plan for tonight?'

'You can get the fucking beers in, you twat.'

'It's for emergencies only,' I countered, 'but I suppose it'd be rude not to furnish the household with a case of premium lagers – share the wealth as they say.'

Looking at the size of my credit limit, I could do some serious damage with this. They even sent me a PIN number for cash withdrawals! Dangerous, very dangerous. Think I might get a phone call from the card issuer if a month's worth of visits to the off-licence appeared on their screens.

**9.30 p.m.** Can't stop thinking of all the things I can do with a £6,000 credit limit. A five-star holiday in the Bahamas? An exotic cruise? It's amazing. With this little card I could walk down to the travel agent tomorrow and book myself a world trip, something that normally requires years of hard saving. 'And how will sir be paying for this transaction?'

'Oh, just put it on my Gold Card.' Ridiculous, utterly ridiculous.

I'm still shocked they let me have a credit card in the first place. I thought these were only for trustworthy customers who could provide financial guarantees, not for handing out to just anybody, particularly a small-time Charlie such as my good self. My mother always said that money burned a hole in my pocket and she was right. Must stop thinking of things I can do with it.

# Do something last minute

*'Say yes to instant gratification.'*

Slogan on *Virgin* Credit Card website, 2006

**Monday 13 May, 2002**

**3.30 p.m. Work.** Woo-hoo! Amster-damage here I come. Big Dave called at lunch to rally the troops with his suggestion for a lads' holiday: 'Alright you prickhouse?'

'Alright you cockhouse, what the hell do you want?'

'Ahhhh, what do I want? What I want to know is how many of you west-country-worzels are up for a bit of Amster-fuckin-damage in a few weeks? We're all earnin' the coin now, 'bout time we had a little reunion – no fuckin' excuses, you're all coming.'

I didn't hesitate for a second.

'Count me in,' I said laughing. 'My flexible friend will take care of it.'

'Good stuff you little mincer, I thought you'd still be crying poor, feed me your usual crap about being skint.'
'Not at all, David, things are looking up at the moment. Just started a new job *and* the bank have given me a Gold Card with *six grand* on it.'

'Six grand, ha ha ha – mental. You can get the beers and skunk in then, Mr Gold Card.'

'Hah – you chief. I'm not gonna burn it, but I am allowing myself this little treat, a working man has a right to such pleasures. I'm well up for it.'

'Know what you're saying mate. Ratboy's already thrown his hat in, so I'll give Pete and Jez a call, then I'll bang an email out with the details.'

'Nice one.'

CLICK!

```
13/05/2002 16:35
From: David Dillon
To: PJ Livingson, Jeremy Boat-Shoes, Pete Perv,
Ratboy, Andy Pandy

Subject: LADS ON TOUR

Dear Mincers,

Get yourselves booked up — details below:
Easyjet GATWICK — SCHIPOL OUT 24.5.02 18:45
SCHIPOL — GATWICK IN 27.5.02 09:05
Hotel is already booked so have your money
ready at the airport.

All my love, Big Dave x x
```

**5.00 p.m.** Oh yes, a holiday at last. This trip will be carnage. With Big Dave at the helm, I'm betting we don't make it out of the red light district. This was just the type of emergency the lady in the bank was talking about. Already got the confirmation email for my flight: 'one click and you're done', as they say.

### Tuesday 28 May, 2002
**11.30 a.m. Work.** God, I feel like shit. Head is still wrecked from puffing the premium grade skunk, been shuffling paper all morning. Late for work as well, but what a weekend. Five go mad in Europe. Jez was the only non-attendee, citing insufficient funds as his excuse. That boy needs to lighten up, learn to live a little. Ah well, his loss.

It was my first experience of a budget airline – like being on a school bus with wings and less legroom. Everything from the plane to the flight attendants was plastered in gaudy orange as if to emphasise the cheapness of the experience. Which is to say there's only one class on EasyJet – riff raff. As we came in to land, a large hen party were drunkenly belting out *Bohemian Rhapsody* at the front of the plane for about the fifth time, and had to be silenced by an irate pilot. Not the type of travel experience you'd associate with membership of the Gold club.

It's one thing to watch a video of girls firing ping-pong balls out of their clackers, another to have them landing in your beer. That *Banana Bar* was one serious deviant parade. Pete'd been banging on about the place ever since we booked up. Each of the women had their own party trick. One girl calling herself 'Love' used her vaginal dexterity to write postcards for people with a chunky marker pen. Another, Leona, could fire a dildo out of her with such force it could break a man's nose. Amster-fuckin-damage indeed.

I was more stoned than pissed at that stage of the evening, and couldn't help but wonder about the women performing the stunts. They'd all clearly seen better days, which made it a bit sad. *They're no different from circus freaks*, I thought, as a tired-looking Thai girl, with a banana protruding from her vagina, lowered herself over another punter to whoops and cheers from his friends.

**1.45 p.m.** Pete's just emailed through some of the photos. My favourite being the shot of Big Dave standing in a giant pair of clogs. At 6'4", with a shaved head, and built like a cage fighter, they almost look the right size for him, although the bright yellow shoes lessen his ferocity somewhat. The tool spent most of the trip strolling around with his shirt off, like he was cruising down the promenade at Skegness. Blessed with our European experience from the student exchange, we tried to tell him it wasn't *de rigueur*. 'The European woman is more sophisticated, David, you won't impress the Dutch girls like that.' But Dave being Dave, he wouldn't have a bar of it, and our protests only served to strengthen his resolve to flaunt his sizeable torso.

**2.15 p.m.** Urrrgh, desperately want to go home. Luckily I've brought my in-flight magazine with me to work. It's crammed full of East European capitals I've never heard of. Plan to skive the afternoon away surfing budget airline destinations. Already had an email from Ratboy asking where we're going next year.

### Wednesday 19 June, 2002
**6.30 p.m. Home.** Stepped in the door to be greeted with my very first credit card bill. Total balance: £700. Ouch! Can't believe I spent that much, but I'm guilty as charged. Thank god the minimum payment's only £25.

### Saturday 22 June, 2002
**6.00 p.m. Bristol: Home.** Woke up this morning and decided today was the day for a shopping spree. Never going to impress the ladies, looking like a charity shop window display. Lord *Ladykiller* Justin would approve of my decision. Allowed myself a cheeky £300 on the card, with the promise to myself that I wouldn't let it go above a grand. Ah, praise be to the minimum payment. I can overhaul my wardrobe and pay it off at my leisure.

**7.30 p.m.** Went a step further and bought a mobile phone to haul myself into the 21st century. Seems you can't do without one these days.

**Sunday 23 June, 2002**

**11.45 a.m. Home.** This has to be the last of it. Did something mental and ordered a top-of-the-range *Pentium 4* laptop which I'll be unwrapping tomorrow morning, courtesy of express delivery service (free on every order above £2,000). Felt a sharp pang of guilt when I pressed 'pay' and saw the confirmation page with the total price. This is most definitely the end of it, the card's being put away now.

**12.30 p.m.** Still feeling a bit dizzy, but surely this is what it's for: being able to buy stuff when you actually need it. And I really needed a new computer. My old relic of a 486 was never built to handle the internet. Hah! No more painfully slow moving between pages. Honestly, how can anyone in the information age question the acquisition of such a powerful tool? Dot.com tycoon Martha Lane Fox wouldn't have thought twice about it. Why, I could be next high-tech millionaire. Can't wait till tomorrow, it feels just like Christmas.

**Monday 24 June, 2002**

**1.30 p.m. Home.** Rang in sick to await delivery of the laptop. Gave the Parcelforce guy a big HO HO HO as he walked up to the door. Grumpy bastard just looked at me blankly, thrusting his electronic pen and LCD pad into my hand, grunting as I handed it back.

**4.30 p.m.** This baby's a serious piece of kick-ass hardware. Spent the last three hours smoking weed and looking at porn amidst a sea of discarded boxes and bubble wrap. It's already occurred to me that this could be the most expensive wank-mag known to man, a little over two grand including all the extras, which by my calculations equates to 571 copies of *Men Only*.

Thursday 27 June, 2002

**6.48 p.m. Home.** My turn to have an appraisal today. A mandatory ritual, treated with derision by management and staff alike, conducted purely to satisfy the demands of Human Resources and corporate protocol. I'd struggled all morning trying to list such things as my strengths, weaknesses and professional goals underneath the various headings on the form my boss had given me. I need not have worried, for it turned out to be a rather peculiar conference, with Mr Townsend preferring to talk about his personal problems rather than my work performance.

The interview took place downstairs in the staff canteen after lunch. I could see that Mr Townsend considered it to be a more convivial setting than one of the formal interview rooms, but it's a dismal environment nonetheless. As is typical of civic buildings, minimal expenditure is committed to the design and fitting out of staff areas. The furniture in this place is tired and morbid and consists of frayed brown sponge chairs arranged around cheap lacquered coffee tables. The foam panels of the false ceiling are unfathomably low, squeezing out space, leaving one feeling stooped and cramped. One must possess the dullest of senses to willingly eat lunch in here, which may explain its popularity with certain members of staff.

We arrived for our little '1–2–1' shortly after the canteen had emptied of people. The poorly ventilated room felt clingy and sickly, still pulsing with the confused odours and warm radiation of recently microwaved food. Only the kitchen attendant in her white serving coat remained, wandering languidly between the tables, carelessly clattering her rattling trolley as she cleared the surfaces of lunchtime debris. I was experiencing my own post-lunch lethargy as we took our seats in the far corner next to the fire exit. I hoped the assessment wouldn't last long.

Adhering to managerial etiquette, Brian had kindly bought us both rank vending-machine coffees, and I reluctantly sipped at the bitter chemical sludge in search of a caffeine boost as we settled in. I wasn't particularly keen to talk about my professional goals as we traded the customary pre-business tittle-tattle and sought to prolong the chatter. Not that keeping Mr Townsend off-topic proved at all difficult. He'd only recently returned to work following a period of stress leave, and was performing his supervisory duties with a noticeable air of indifference. Sitting across from him like this, I was able to study him closely. Gaunt and unhealthy-looking, he had the appearance of a troubled man. His skin was flaky and pockmarked, and as he spoke, he looked at me with dull, lifeless eyes. A small thin man, he was unable to hide behind his physical attributes, and the baggy suit, which shrouded his meagre frame, made him appear ghostly.

Mr Townsend seemed surprisingly eager to talk about his difficulties. Ignoring my appraisal sheet, he began by telling me how he was trying to negotiate an early release, by which he meant retirement. He'd had enough, he told me bluntly. Didn't enjoy the job, hated it even, a remark I found privately amusing given the context of our interview. I was still absorbing his unprompted diatribe as he started speaking again, telling me in a low, tired voice how he didn't feel enthusiastic about anything and that he found getting out of bed almost impossible on some mornings. He mentioned his children, told me how they were the only thing keeping him going. I hadn't expected to be subjected to such an emotional outpouring on the part of my manager, and tried as best I could to appear unruffled.

I must've been doing well at playing the part of the good listener. I'd contributed little more than a few appropriately timed, neutral remarks, and yet he proceeded to tell me in unreserved detail about his divorce and subsequent breakdown. I learnt that his wife, ten years his junior, had left him for another man. In his weary monotone, he told me how he'd happily indulged her desire to re-train as a teacher only for her to announce, shortly after qualifying, that she was leaving him for a colleague at the local school. To compound his misery, his estranged wife was now living with her new lover less than a mile away from him in the same village. I noticed his small bony hands tremble as he spoke, and thought he might spill his coffee as he shakily raised the plastic cup to his lips. The only bright spot in his wretched tale was that his teenage daughters had elected to remain with their father.

The poor man was clearly too traumatised to contain himself, and I listened attentively to his litany of very personal revelations. I felt genuine sympathy for him, although I couldn't help wondering why he'd chosen to confide in me like this. All things considered, I was an unusual choice of confidant. Maybe he was worried about office gossip. He'd already told me that he didn't have any real friends here, just 'circumstantial associates'. I was aware that he'd been fairly ruthless in his ascent up the ladder and knew he was disliked by some of the older heads. Perhaps he was trying to get me on-side? Regardless of his motives, the conversation was at the very least genuine. Mr Townsend was being refreshingly candid, and despite his suicidal tone, it was much better than talking about work. I'd even begun asking gently probing questions so as not to make him feel uncomfortable.

With barely any prompting, Mr Townsend started telling me about his months of stress leave. There were days when he'd neglected to get dressed, he said, weeks where he'd hardly left the house. He'd done nothing but think and reflect on his life. He'd worked hard for the sake of his family, chasing promotions, putting in the hours and sacrificing his own aspirations. I got the impression he'd pandered to his younger spouse with the ever-increasing anxiety of the older man. He made no attempt to disguise his resentment and said, quite forcibly, that he'd wasted his life on this woman. Again he remarked how he didn't care for the job, that he wished he'd done something different with his years. He hadn't the energy or desire to start again. For the first time in the conversation I felt uneasy as the flicker of tacit understanding registered between us: this was a tired middle-aged man with no hopes – and worst of all he knew it.

There followed a brief pause, long enough for me to make a youthfully arrogant vow not to end up like the man before me. Mr Townsend seemed to be trying to gather himself. His experiences had clearly affected him badly and recounting them was causing him some distress. I watched as he nervously patted his hair, smoothing the thin strands in a sideways motion across his blotchy scalp. He licked his lips several times, like a sickly animal about to vomit, before he leant across the table towards me, closing the void between us so I could smell the stale coffee on his breath. I held my position as our eyes locked, resisting the urge to sit back in my chair. In a tone of bitter and broken insistence, his voice wavering and unsteady, he began giving me advice, urging me to be selfish, to always do what I wanted. He was beginning to babble and I thought he might break down in front of me. I felt paralysed, and remained rigid as he continued, unable to look away as he gave me a warning about putting my faith in people or my career. I had no idea how I was meant to respond to this and was desperately trying to think of something to say. Whether he sensed my discomfort, I don't know, but he seemed to catch himself and made to apologise. I waved my hand dismissively to show it was alright, but Mr Townsend had already stood up. Stuttering and looking distractedly around the room, he apologised, telling me not to take any notice of him. Then he excused himself, and I watched him shuffle agitatedly across the room. He really wasn't well enough to be at work, I thought. He needed help.

Waiting for him to return, I thought about all the hours he had probably spent alone at home, corrosively chewing over his situation. The crisis had caused him to confront things and he was acutely aware of his life's failings. Everything he'd worked for and placed his faith in had proved useless. Without the consolation of family life, his existence had revealed itself for exactly what it was – pointless and vacant. I thought about him spending three decades of his life in this dismal building. I couldn't imagine such a thing, no wonder he was desperate to get out. Each additional day must've been an unbearable, mocking reminder of his foolishness. It then occurred to me that perhaps he had seen himself in me, hence the pep talk – an idea I found unsettling and slightly repulsive.

I looked up and saw the door open again, and I watched as he made his way back towards me. As he sat down, he seemed calmer. In light of our discussion, I felt that I could be honest, so I told him I didn't much care for the appraisal. He couldn't really argue and agreed to sign it off without reading it. The meeting was over and as we walked back to our floor he seemed a little uneasy about our talk. I assured him, quite sincerely, that it would remain private, that I hadn't the slightest inclination to betray his confidence.

I returned to my seat, but switching back into work mode was impossible. I couldn't get Mr Townsend out of my head, and kept sneaking looks at him. I was unable to shake the notion of myself as a younger version of my boss, and comforted myself with the fact that time was on my side. But it didn't work. I began to panic until I just couldn't sit there any longer. I grabbed my things, made an excuse to Mr Townsend about a forgotten doctor's appointment and headed straight home.

### Friday 5 July, 2002
**9.15 a.m. Bristol: doormat.** Oh dear, my second credit card bill. Already. It's going to take at least a year to get that little lot paid off.

### Wednesday 17 July, 2002
**7.15 p.m. Bristol: home.** Aunty Marge's prophecy continues to come true. Had another emergency when I ran out of real money and had to resort to a cash withdrawal on the Gold Card to tide me over until payday. What a wonderful facility.

### Friday 9 August, 2002
**9.30 a.m. Bristol: home.** Awoke to the loud thump of a heavy parcel landing on the doormat. Began the day by unwrapping my latest batch of CDs – the entire *Smiths* back catalogue. Jez introduced me to the world of online auctions and I've become an Ebay junky. Every day is like Christmas and between us we're keeping the postman busy. 'Presents to

ourselves,' we like to say. The prick has even been lauding his Feedback Status over me: his star's turned blue whereas mine's still yellow. Twat. I'll catch him soon.

### Monday 1 September, 2002
**10.30 a.m. Work.** Somebody up there loves me. Walked into the news that the results of an internal pay review will see the whole department upgraded. Thought everybody looked unusually happy for a Monday morning. It's not everyday you get given a four-grand pay rise!

**10.35 a.m.** I've got the Midas touch… Everything I touch turns to gold.

**2.30 p.m.** Celebrated my windfall by placing a series of unbeatable bids on a set of first edition Charles Bukowski novels.

### Sunday 22 September, 2002
**8.30 p.m. Bristol.** *'First make a list of your strengths and weaknesses. When you have done this sit down and identify your goals. What is it that YOU WANT out of life? You know what you want, NOW spell it out for yourself.'*

'What the fuck is this?' I said, looking across at Rick in the driver's seat. He was laughing as the calm but assertive voice of an American business guru filled the car.

'Be quiet mate, don't interrupt Kenneth K. Klein, you might learn something.'

*'Now you can match your abilities to your aims,'* the voice continued. *'You have the weapons in your hand, now it is time to wield them…'*

'Enough,' I cried, covering my ears in simulated agony.

Rick hit the mute button. 'I knew you'd be impressed,' he said sarcastically.

He dug down in the door pocket beside him and handed me the CD case. '*Wake Up and Sell the Coffee – How to Achieve Everything You Wanted and More*' by Kenneth K. Klein. On the back was a photograph of a bespectacled nerd who looked a lot like Bill Gates, standing outside a mock-Gothic mansion.

'He's a self-made multi-millionaire,' explained Rick.

'He's a total poindexter,' I said jumping in.

'Well he's a very rich poindexter,' Rick countered immediately. 'I've been reading a lot of business motivation books lately. You have to think outside the box if you want to get ahead. He's in London next week, I'm going to his seminar at Earls Court.'

'You're fucking crazy,' I screamed. He hadn't completely flipped, he knew it was funny and was laughing with me.

'Anyway, where are we going now?' I asked. He'd taken me out for a spin in his new company BMW and we'd reached the other side of town.

'Don't worry, we're nearly there.'

'Nearly where?'

'If I told you that it wouldn't be a surprise would it?' he said as he took a turn into the Semilong district.

'Are we going on a whore tour?' I said, as we passed the truckers' stop on the edge of Semilong that served as the main source of business for the town's red light district.

Rick shook his head.

We took the next right and drove halfway up the street, before he stopped the car and reversed into a space. As we stepped out, two teenage boys on bikes skidded to a halt by the car. Rick clicked the electronic key to lock up and the lads made a big play of admiring the sleek black 5–Series.

'Hey mister, you want us to look after your car,' chirped the slightly older-looking boy.

'Nothing's gonna happen to this car,' said Rick firmly. The boys stared back at him.

'Fiver each and we'll make sure nobody touches it,' offered the same boy.

Rick ignored him and walked up the steps of one of the terrace houses. I followed behind.

'Is this where your mistress lives?' I enquired.

'Fuck's sake mate, you know I'm a one-woman man,' he said annoyed at my questioning his strict moral code.

He pulled a set of keys from his pocket and opened the door before stepping inside. The first thing that hit me was the stench, like a truck of rotting fruit. I covered my nostrils as we walked into the lounge. The place was vacant although it was clear somebody had lived there until very recently.

'Aargh, what the fuck is that smell?' I cried, feeling my stomach convulse and turning to leave.

'Bloody cleaners!' howled Rick, hurriedly following me back out. 'They were supposed to come yesterday.' Then he clamped his hand over his nose as he yanked the door shut and locked up again.

'Who the hell lives here?' I squealed.

Rick was seething, unable to answer. He stood there for a minute with his hands on his hips cursing, dismayed that we couldn't go inside.

'We bought the place at auction about two weeks ago,' he began to explain, before pausing, still trying to compose himself. 'Some old boy died in there, apparently he'd been there about a month before anyone noticed. That's why we paid to have the place fumigated.'

I stood with my hands in my pockets and lifted my eyebrows by way of response.

'Fucking hell!' he shouted angrily, kicking the wall. His surprise had been spoilt.

'First thing tomorrow I'm phoning that fucking cleaning company to give 'em a rollicking.'

We climbed back into the car. The two boys were on the other side of the street, still watching us and looking slightly bemused.

'At least you don't have to worry about squatters,' I jested, as Rick pulled out into the road aggressively, with the tyres screeching.

He wasn't in the mood for jokes, and refused to crack a smile. His tantrums had always been a great source of amusement to us over the years and made him an easy target for wind-ups. He'll definitely have to watch the blood pressure when he's older.

'Fucking Polish bastards,' he cursed, still furious, slamming the car to an abrupt halt at the junction.

'What would Kenneth Klein do now?' I said, unable to resist another gag.

'Seriously mate, fuck off.'

As we headed back towards his other house he managed to simmer down a bit and explained his strategy for achieving everything he wanted and more.

'We bought the place on buy-to-let. We're gonna subdivide the bedrooms and rent it out to students. In 30 years when the mortgage is paid off, it'll be ours to sell. Property's the best investment you can make.'

'Oh my god, stop,' I pleaded. 'You sound just like my father.' If I didn't know better, I'd swear our parents had met on the swinging circuit back in the day, I was beginning to suspect that Rick was my dad's love child.

'Buy land, because they ain't making any more of it. You know who said that?' asked Rick, as he shifted through the gears and sped down the dual carriageway.

'Mark Twain,' I said despondently. It pained me to hear him quoting Huck Finn's creator like that. There's nothing stopping the business gurus of the world bastardising the wisdom of the greats.

'This is just the start. It's all about making property work for you.'

I sank into my seat and let him talk.

'Things are going well at ADS, and our division's the top performing arm in the company. My boss said that if my level of business continues, I'll be made a partner in two years. They're big on setting goals, it really motivates people. I've been putting in the graft, doing 10-hour days and working an 11-day fortnight. It's hard missing out on things, so I make sure I go for it when I get the chance. Work hard, play hard, that's my motto.'

He sniffed.

'Abby's accepted I'll be working a lot. But the big plan is for me to be retired by 40 and out on the golf course.'

'But you don't play golf,' I said.

'I do now, mate. The biggest deals are done on the golf course. You can't afford not to play. I've been taking lessons.'

'Does Kenneth Klein play golf?'

'Handicap of five,' he said, turning to me with a broad smile. He'd cheered up a bit, having talked himself around.

We'd done with cruising around and made for the station, since it was time for me to catch my train home to Bristol. The conversation changed course.

'You got yourself another woman yet?' asked Rick.

'Not yet, not really.'

'What about your mates, you still living together?'

'Yeah, it's bachelor central. It's killing me getting up for work every other day with a hangover.'

'Ha ha, I have to admire you mate, you're still clinging to your student days. You won't be able to keep it going, you'll get sick of it soon. I've knocked the drink on the head during the week. I can't afford to be off-colour. I save it all for the weekends now.'

We parted company for another few months, as I ran for my train. It was a bright September day; the country was enjoying an Indian Summer. Onboard, the carriage was warm and fusty. I nestled into my seat and prepared myself for an afternoon doze. As the train creaked out of the station, I looked out at the town, at all the rows of neat houses bathed in golden light. It looked quiet and peaceful, like it was resting, waiting for something.

I thought about Rick's comment as the vehicle rocked slowly from side to side. Maybe I was clinging to my student days. Should I be embarrassed about it, I wondered. My head felt heavy, my thoughts loose. He was right, I definitely seemed to be railing against something. I put my feet up on the seat opposite and stretched my legs as the train gained momentum. The answer lay in front of me as I squinted out of the window through tired eyelids. It was there in the tidy streets and the orderly lives of this provincial town: a pointless collection of people scurrying home every night to sit in front of the TV, making sure they went to bed early in readiness for work the next day. Life isn't what you can cram into two days of leisure, I thought to myself as I finally succumbed, closing my eyes and slipping into a beautiful, dreamy sleep. It can't be.

### Wednesday 16 October, 2002

**9.15 a.m. Doormat.** Another bill. The blasted things are now arriving with a prompt regularity I'm beginning to dread. That total balance just keeps on *a-rising*. I must be alright though, the bank have extended my limit without my asking them to. Well, they wouldn't be lending it if I couldn't afford it. Made a promise to myself: the minimum payment can't exceed £200.

### Thursday 14 November, 2002

**5.45 p.m. Bristol: Home.** Had an incredibly embarrassing conversation with a girl from the credit card company, thanks to Pete. After several failed attempts to cancel the £30-a-month Russian porn site subscription, I had no choice but to terminate things at my end. I could hear the girl at the other end sniggering to her mate in the call centre as I tried to convince her that my housemate had signed me up to 'Pandora's Triple-X Palace'.

### Tuesday 17 December, 2002

**8.00 p.m. Bristol: Home.** Ratboy's been on the phone trying to pressure the Bristol connection into joining him and Big Dave on a snowboarding trip to Austria in the New Year. Have rebuffed the offer due to prohibitive cost: £1,500 all in, he reckons.

**Friday 20 December, 2002**

**6.00 p.m. Bristol: Home.** Knackered! Left my Christmas shopping to the last minute as usual. Shops were hell. Bought Mum an enormous Edward Hopper print in the hope of dislodging St Paul from his perch in the living room. Got a bit carried away in the end, the folks are getting a lot from me this year. Neh well, this isn't the time to be worrying about the bill. As the man on the BBC said this morning, everyone overspends at Christmas: 'tis the season to be merry after all. Like the rest of my card-carrying compatriots, I'll deal with it in the New Year.

# A Serious Habit

*'Credit card cheques tend to be marketed vigorously by issuers. This may encourage consumers to use them without fully appreciating the consequences. They may also be encouraged to use cheques in inappropriate circumstances, for example, to pay utility bills.'*

Office of Fair Trading report on the Use of Credit Card Cheques, 2006

**Friday 3 January, 2003**

**11.45 p.m. Bristol: Home. A deeper shade of lilac.** Just got back into town after the festive break. Met a new girl at a party and we seem to have clicked right away, the only downer being that she lives in London. Might prove tricky in the long term. Her name's Kelly and she's a singer in a rock band, so god knows what she sees in a pikey council worker with a penchant for matching shirt and tie sets.

Mental note: *never* allow her to see you in work attire. She must never set eyes on the clown-clobber. Thanks to my ever-considerate mother, her bright young success story has three new shirt sets from Next, in *three* different shades of lilac.

**Tuesday 14 January, 2003**

**9.15 p.m. Bristol: Home.** Completely shattered. Spent the weekend in London, gallivanting with Kelly. Drove up to her flat in Wood Green after work on Friday. We've been speaking on the phone all week and just had to see each other. Feels like there's a real connection. On the few occasions we managed to make it out of the bedroom, I was like a wide-eyed child staring up at all the buildings and bright lights. There's a definite buzz about it and I'm already hooked.

Felt like the King of Cool cruising the bars and cafés with an indie-rock singer on my arm. I can't keep my hands off her. I'm a sucker for long blonde hair, and her short curvy figure begs to be touched, regardless of whether we're in public or not. She really is my kind of girl, always looking effortlessly alternative in her collection of second-hand clothes and homemade outfits. She's genuine too, not one of those £500 'Bohemians' you see getting about these days, the type who pay through their noses to look offbeat.

As the weekend drew to a close, we sat huddled together in the corner of the local pub until closing time on Sunday, getting slowly sozzled on pints of Carlsberg Export, trading love-struck compliments and talking about our dreams. I'm sure we must've been turning the barman's stomach with our incessant smooching. Cashed in my exemplary attendance record at work by calling in sick on Monday to prolong the fantasy. Flying high at the moment.

### Thursday 16 January, 2003
**11.00 p.m. Bristol: Home.** Spending over an hour every night on the phone to my new love. Amazing, the things you find to talk about. Phone bill promises to be huge.

### Saturday 18 January, 2003
**6.38 p.m. Kelly's flat.** Back in London already. This cat can't keep away. Met up with Ratboy and Big Dave in Camden while Kelly was at the studio, rehearsing with the band. They double-teamed me and I've pathetically capitulated over the Austria trip. It's all happening at once and I'd probably say yes to anything in my current frame of mind.

Certainly never stood a chance in the face of a bit of peer pressure. The Rat started in by loudly announcing to the table how I was scared of falling over and hurting myself. Every time I opened my mouth to counter him, he just made 'meowing' sounds at me.

'Look, I really can't afford it,' I protested over his mewling. 'I've been caning the plastic, I need to start paying it off.' 'Purrrr, purrrr, Meeeeeow…' Everybody was listening to his baiting now, I didn't know most of his mates and already I was a laughing stock.

'Fuck off, you little rat,' I spat, trying to get him to back off. At times like this, he fully deserved his unfortunate nickname: skinny little Ratboy with his greasy dark hair and pointy features, always ready to sell you out for a cheap laugh.

Big Dave joined in the chorus and they began singing in unison. I sheepishly sipped at my pint waiting for the cat choir to finish goading me. A couple of his mates were chuckling to themselves, eager to see if I'd crack.

'One more trip won't kill you. Pay it off when you get back. You'll miss out on all the fun,' reasoned Big Dave. 'There's no way you can owe as much as I do, so you've got no excuse.'

'You reckon! I've already spunked a few grand and I've only had it a few months. I need to get it under control before it gets out of hand.'

'Well one more won't make much difference will it? Ha ha. All you gotta do is keep shifting the balances around. That way you don't pay any interest. I've got about ten grand on the fuckers, costs me fuck all though.' He made it sound easy. 'Ahhhh, I get it. You've got a new girlfriend and she won't let you go! Is that a giant thumbprint on your forehead?' They both pressed their thumbs to their foreheads, causing the rest of the table to begin wetting themselves. It was too much to take.

'Right, right, that's it, fuck you, you pricks, I'm coming.'

They certainly know which buttons to push. I've spent the rest of the day beating myself up for being so bloody weak-willed. But there's no backing out now.

### Monday 20 January, 2003

**11.15 a.m. Bristol: Work.** Ratboy sent through details of the snowboarding trip. Felt seriously guilty reading out my card details to the travel agent.

**11.25 a.m.** Now I'm excited. Never been on a winter holiday before. All the email banter's begun over who'll be the worst boarder.

### Saturday 25 January, 2003
**7.36 p.m. London: Kelly's flat.** This girl is amazing. Couldn't resist driving up to see her again. Costing a fortune in petrol. Also spent the afternoon in Covent Garden with Ratboy plundering the ski shops, getting ourselves kitted out for Austria. A moneyless man goes fast through the market – but the man with a pocketful of credit…

### Sunday 26 January, 2003
**11.30 p.m. London.** Stayed up till 3 a.m. with Kelly, drinking wine and talking, before I met the band today. Hung out at their jam, smoking weed and sinking beers down at the studios. Totally exhilarating watching them rock out. If I'm honest I'm a bit blown away. The past few weeks have been intoxicating. Work is but an inconvenient distraction – planning another sickie tomorrow, the weekends just aren't long enough.

### Monday 27 January, 2003
**11.05 a.m. The Joy of Sick.** Called the office earlier to register my absence. Danced a jig of delight after doing the deed, before bundling back into bed. When I'd done dozing again, the first thing I thought about was my empty chair in the office. It brought a smile to my face as I pictured my co-workers busying around my little island of indolence.

It's an indisputable fact that there's infinitely more pleasure to be derived from a stolen day than any sanctioned leave.

Going out this afternoon. No need to worry about a disguise either – little chance of being spotted when you're two hundred miles from the office.

**Sunday 2 February, 2003**

**2.30 p.m. Kelly's flat.** Wow. I thought I'd seen it all down at rehearsals, but that was another level, watching my new girlfriend rock on stage in front of an audience. From the first number right through to the last, I stood in disbelief as she threw herself around and belted out the songs. Hearing all the cheers and applause made my hair stand on end. At one point I even felt like crying.

In fact, I feel a bit miserable now. I keep asking myself, what does she see in me? I'm certainly no guitar hero. When I first told Jez about Kelly he went straight in for the kill: 'You might have a pretty face but you'll do well to keep hold of her,' he said with his customary bluntness. '*I* know!' he continued wickedly. 'Why don't you hammer out a tune for her with your scale ruler and council clipboard?'

I put it down to a touch of jealousy, and tried not to let him see he'd gotten to me. He's right though, maybe this time I'll be the one on the receiving end of the big heave-ho. I guess this is what happens, when you find someone you really like. You become vulnerable, you develop a weak point that wasn't there before.

**Sunday 9 February, 2003**

**11.45 a.m. Bristol.** The trials of a long-distance relationship. We couldn't see each other this weekend, because Kelly's got back-to-back rehearsals and it was Jez's birthday bash last night. So I've spent the last two days in irrational turmoil, battling a severe case of paranoia. When I rang her phone last night it went straight to voicemail. Hoping she'd just forgotten to charge it.

**12.30 p.m.** I don't think I'm strong enough to cope with this mentally. Most of the time I feel on top of the world, the happiest man alive. But then there are times, like now, when my stomach's in knots. I think about it all going awry and feel physically sick. Maybe I've read it wrong and been getting carried away, after all it's barely been six weeks. Perhaps this was just meant to be a brief fling?

**1.30 p.m.** Jez isn't helping matters: 'You've got a face like a wet weekend, what's wrong with you? You're like a lovesick puppy, checking your phone every five minutes – snap out of it.'

**3.30 p.m.** Kelly called: 'You silly boy, of course I still like you.' There's no reception in the basement studio. Of course, I've been there, I should know. Have arranged to stop by her place for a few days before the ski-trip next week. Ahhh, back on top again.

### Friday 21 February, 2003

**11.23 p.m. London: Kelly's flat.** Ooooooooo! Think I need a liver transplant. Kitzbühel was a blast. Seventeen of us out on the slopes all day and partying well into the next morning. Kelly cringed when I told her how we'd all done 'the conga' through the middle of town. The boys were right, it was worth it, definitely the most fun I've had on holiday. Not cheap though, reckon I blew nearly two grand in all. But how can you put a price on good times and memories?

### Sunday 23 February, 2003

**12.45 a.m. Kelly's flat.** A freezing winter's day. Nothing but grey clouds and cold winds, perfect for remaining in bed till lunchtime. The two of us spent several frisky hours under the covers and had a deliciously raunchy conversation, confessing our deepest fantasies to one another. And it's given me the most brilliant idea. Been up with a glass of wine while my lover sleeps soundly, penning an erotic story based on one of her scenarios. It's getting me worked up just thinking about it. Can't wait to hear her reaction when she gets this in the post. Hah! It's one way of keeping a long distance relationship strong, and a good way to ward off predatory guitar strummers.

I think I've found my calling: P. J. Livingson – secret writer of erotic letters.

### Tuesday 25 February, 2003

**9.20 a.m. Bristol: Doormat.** Gulp! It's that time already. The monthly statement drops through the door. I can hardly bear to look.

**9.25 a.m.** Jesus Fucking Christ.

**9.30 p.m.** Made the mistake of telling Jez about the size of my credit card bill. He can be such a fucking puritan sometimes. He took great pleasure in calculating that I've been living above my means to the tune of £500 a month since I got the card. Nobody likes a smart arse, particularly a smart arse economics student. Unbelievably, he proceeded to climb onto his soapbox and started preaching about the pitfalls of debt, at which point I told him in no uncertain words to butt out.

He hasn't a clue about the real world. Typical of a public schoolboy. He plays the dropout type very well, slumming it with the state schoolers, but when you get to know him, you discover he's a lot more prudent than he cares to let on. I remember the day we discovered he'd invested his student loans in stocks and shares, and there he was cadging pints off us after his allowance had run out. The wealthiest are always the tightest.

### Thursday 27 February, 2003
**6.30 p.m. Bristol.** My racy missive has been dispatched. Popped it in the post this afternoon. Kelly's in for one hell of a surprise, I haven't said a word about my secret endeavours. Hope she likes it.

### Friday 28 February, 2003
**12.30 p.m. Bristol: Office.** Woke up today and the first thing I thought about was Kelly collecting her post and the look on her face when she opened the envelope. I'd just parked up when my phone rang.

'It's brilliant baby, what a lovely surprise.'

I was laughing excitedly, I'd been praying it would work. 'Have you read all of it?' I asked eagerly.

'I read the first page on the tube to work. It made me feel really naughty sitting amongst all those people, reading something like that. I'm saving the rest for when I get home tonight.'

'Are you really?' I said suggestively.

'I am indeed, I'm looking forward to reading it in bed later,' she said knowingly.

'Brilliant,' I exclaimed, jiggling my legs in triumphant glee.

'It's really well written, I hope the rest of it's like that. You've got a real talent here.'

Hearing this put me up in the clouds.

'You better get yourself up here tomorrow if you know what's good for you.'

I've been delighting in my accomplishment all morning. If I could high-five myself I would do so. Yea-fuckin-ha!

**Monday 3 March, 2003**
**11.30 p.m. Home.** Met up with Justin tonight at the god-awful Scream Bar. He insisted on this characterless theme bar due to its popularity with students. He was celebrating buying a flat. I knew there was no chance Greyweather could've given him a pay rise and it turns out he just lied about his income on the mortgage application. The advice from his financial advisor of all people was that it's easy to blag as they never check up. Providing you can afford the monthly payment, there's no problem with it. Justin was giving it the large one about how his mate had written a dodgy letter saying he was an employee of his company and that he earned £30,000 a year, twice his real income! He even forged a couple of payslips. It was that easy. He received confirmation this morning and has just been loaned four times his 'salary'.

Next to us at the bar, a group of student girls were buying rounds of brightly coloured vodka shots in test tubes. Lord Ladykiller ordered a whole rack, distributing them among the grateful young mouths before handing me a luminous green cylinder to toast his acquisition. I then had to suffer hearing him prematurely invite them all to his house-warming.

**Tuesday 4 March, 2003**
**3.15 p.m. Bristol: Office. Easy decision – 4\* Venice, Hard Decision – Espresso or Latte?** What better antidote to the interminable winter than a dose of *La Dolce Vita*? About to embark on my second out-of-season sojourn in the space of three weeks. Decided to spring a surprise for my new girl with a weekend in Europe. And could there be a more fitting

destination than Venice, the capital of romance? A suitable stage is required, as I plan to tell her how I feel. The *pièce de resistance* being that I'm refusing to disclose the destination until we get to the airport. Can't wait to see her face! My mother calls it 'the pink mist' and I'm certainly riding the wave of new relationship euphoria – all the way to the departure lounge.

**4.25 p.m.** Having announced my latest holiday plans, the collective envy of my colleagues is palpable. It seems the only limit to my ambitions is my annual leave allowance.

### Thursday 6 March, 2003
**5.30 p.m. London: Kelly's flat.** Spent a few days cavorting around London before the flight tomorrow. The holiday's already begun: saw a few bands at the Borderline last night, went to the Tate Modern today, followed by a slap-up Italian in Soho – acclimatising for the weekend, Cameriere!

**10.30 p.m.** The alarm's set for an early start. Kelly still hasn't a clue where she's going and keeps begging me for clues. Am loving holding all the cards. I know she's thinking along the lines of Paris, Rome, Madrid, so planning to get in the queue for Dublin for a laugh.

### Monday 10 March, 2003
**9.30 p.m. Bristol: Home.** Venice was a roaring success and we are officially in love. It was a faltering, nervous confession, which came in the departure lounge whilst waiting for our flight home. I've never put myself on the line like that before and had spent the whole weekend plucking up the courage. Worn out emotionally and physically, we both collapsed into our seats and only awoke as we touched down at Stansted.

Kelly was suitably impressed with the destination. Felt completely at home amongst the tactile Italians. When they're not posing behind their over-sized sunglasses waiting to be noticed, they're shamelessly groping one another in the middle of the street. All weekend we kept laughing at the same things, like the performance of a little girl at the airport, who theatrically spat out green olives that her tired parents tried to persuade her to eat. By the end we couldn't look at her without wetting ourselves. Precious moments.

### Friday 14 March, 2003
**9.15 a.m. Bristol: Doormat.** I have a new dirty secret: my outstanding balance. Been sweeping the bills under the metaphorical carpet as thinking about them just makes me anxious. Also hiding the statements from Jez, as he keeps making unsettling remarks about my lifestyle, sounding disturbingly like my father.

Speaking of the old fella, he's been getting suspicious of all my 'fancy holidays'. Fobbed him off with a load of flannel about the new era of low-cost travel redefining the concept of leisure. A member of the Caravan Club for thirty years, he thinks EasyJet is some sort of carwash.

### Sunday 30 March, 2003
**10.45 p.m. London: Kelly's new flat.** Helping Kelly move house this weekend. She's really stretched herself following her friends to Kensington. Had to lend her £500 for the deposit. We're a terrible combination – both live for the moment and useless with money. Nice place though, it's even got a terrace for *al fresco* breakfasting.

**Thursday 3 April, 2003**

**1.30 p.m. Bristol: Bed.** Been on the sick all week with a fictitious bout of summer flu. Who says the British don't know how to live? Here I am, frolicking under the covers with a girl in the middle of the working day, guzzling Champagne and scoffing strawberries. Kelly arrived last Saturday and I've taken the opportunity to show her my town. Yesterday we took a picnic and hiked across the Clifton Suspension Bridge to spend the day stretched out under a tree in Ashton Court park, overlooking the bowl of the city.

Have also been paying to dine out every evening, as Jez is angling to show off his culinary skills before I've had a chance to dazzle her with mine. A small price to pay for kitchen kudos. Despite Jeremy's ridiculously forced attempts to act cool and make me look like an idiot in front of Kelly, with his references to clipboards and scale rulers, he's failing miserably.

'He's such a caricature,' remarked Kelly. 'Those clothes are awful.' She was referring to Jez's inability to break with the uniform of the moneyed classes: the Ralph Lauren polo shirts neatly tucked into faded jeans, complimented by the mandatory loafers.

'I can't wait to tell him that when you're gone,' I said, delighted with the ammunition she'd just given me.

'Oh no, you can't,' she pleaded. 'He's lovely really, he'll hate me. Tell him I said he's got strong features.'

**Monday 7 April 2003**

**10.30 a.m. Bristol: Work.** Taken aside by the boss for a 'quick word in private'. The charge sheet included 'a series of absences', 'general timekeeping issues' and 'a dip in performance'. It was a half-hearted ticking-off from Mr Townsend. The hierarchy have ceded to his retirement pleas and he's literally counting the days till his pension.

### Monday 21 April, 2003
**4.30 p.m. Bristol: Home.** Arrived back from London more tired than ever. Up at 5.15 a.m. in a bid to get to work on time following recent reprimand. Drove down the motorway at 90mph with the window down, pumped up on rank service station espresso to keep from falling asleep. Since the turn of the year, I've been living in two places. Something has to give. Ended up booking a phoney meeting and parking up in a lay-by for some much needed shut-eye.

### Monday 12 May, 2003
**11.30 a.m. Bristol: Work.** Had to give Kelly another handout this morning before I left. She's straight into the overdraft once her rent's paid.

### Wednesday 21 May, 2003
**2.45 p.m. Bristol: Work.** My head is elsewhere at the moment. Even the most perfunctory tasks require superhuman effort. If I'm not busy composing my daily email to Kelly, then I'm lost in thought wondering what to write in my next one. Sometimes I panic and get paranoid that some snooper in the IT department has been reading all my soul-baring messages out to all the other gimps in their office. They could be having a right laugh acting out our parts.

### Tuesday 27 May, 2003
**9.45 a.m. Doormat.** Hooooooo! Broke out in a cold sweat after opening my latest bill. Another credit limit reached and

breached. Actually feel like puking. It seems impossible I've spent all of it – and so soon. It's only taken a couple of holidays and a few weekends in London. Jez is right, been living way above my means, going to look very stupid when it all comes crashing down around me – he'll be the first to say *I told you so*.

**9.55 a.m.** This is a wake-up call. It's not too late to do something about it. Like going upstairs right now and cutting the blasted thing up. That's what I'll do, destroy the card before I change my mind.

**11.30 a.m. Work.** Sat on the bed earlier, card and scissors in hand. Felt like a gibbering crackhead contemplating one last hit. All I had to do was close my eyes and SNIP! The spell would've been broken. But I just couldn't go through with it. Instead I sat there thinking about life without it, as though I were considering severing a limb. My earlier resolve had begun to fade, giving way to twisted, flawed logic: 'after all, I could easily order a replacement'. I put the scissors down and got up to leave for work with the card back in my wallet.

**11.45 a.m. Work.** Bugger me. This morning's drama could've been avoided. Making the call to pay the bill I suddenly noticed the line at the bottom: *You have £2,300 available to spend.*

They've only increased my limit again. I'm saved! How the hell did I fail to spot it earlier? Never mind, feel better now. It's good to know there's money if I need it. Still going to be sensible. Like no more cash withdrawals. Have developed a nasty habit of squaring my current account with cash from the credit card to avoid being hit with bank charges.

### Thursday 29 May, 2003

**11.45 p.m. Home. Burp!** Just returned from a night down the local with Justin. He's moved into his new place. Felt better about finances when he confessed to living half the month on his cards. 'That makes two of us,' I said, and so we drank to that and the benefits of minimum payments.

### Sunday 1 June, 2003

**7.30 p.m. London: Kelly's flat.** Big decision time – I'm following my heart and moving to London. I was still a little apprehensive as to Kelly's reaction. Things couldn't be better between us, but a small part of me worried even she might think it a step too far. Thankfully she was delighted when I broached the subject in the pub earlier, instantly throwing herself at me, nearly sending our drinks flying. We sat there wrapped up in each other, talking about all the things we were going to do when I got my move, only breaking our embrace when we had to answer the call of nature.

**8.00 p.m.** I still have to pinch myself. My life's been turned upside down in a matter of weeks. I wasn't looking for this, you think you're in control of your life and then – wham! But I wouldn't have it any other way. I've been dealt a good hand and I'd be a fool to throw it away.

**8.15 p.m.** This feels so right. I've been completely exhausted living in two places at once, and weekends in the big city don't fit a salary in the provinces. Figure I can calm down the spending if I'm living in one place. We're both really excited. Job-hunting starts tomorrow.

**9.30 p.m.** Called Pete in Bristol to tell him of my decision. He had some news of his own. He's off travelling with Ratboy at the end of the year. They've been threatening to do it for a while and plan to tour Asia before settling in Australia. He's had enough of alarm clocks, grumpy bosses, long hours, dark days with endless rain and, as he put it, 'stuck-up women obsessed with status and shopping'. It's not been running for him lately, and he's packing his rucksack, heading off in search of something better. And good luck to him. He's seen the haggard look of the 50-year-old British worker and he's getting out. 'You only live once,' he said. Who am I to argue with that?

**Monday 9 June, 2003**
**11.30 p.m. Bristol: Home.** Back from London. Kelly was skint so I made like a modern-day hunter-gatherer by taking her to Safeway to stock her cupboards. Couldn't bear to see her starve.

**Wednesday 25 June, 2003**
**8.30 p.m. Bristol: Home.** 'Alright ya two-bob?' Big Dave on the phone.

'Alright you queen?'

'Now listen up, I've been chatting to the Rat and we're up for going away in a few weeks. Last chance for a Lads' Tour with everyone together, before the boys head off.'

'Okay…'

'Up for a bit of Prague action geez? Mate of mine just got back, said it was fuckin' wicked, 30p pints, luvvly east Euro birds in the clubs, few lap dances, cheeky little fondle, you know the score,' he said with a growl and a seedy laugh that made him sound like a Soho porn peddler.

'Bit strapped at the moment, mate. Not sure if I can do another holiday,' I said, with my sensible head on.

'Same 'ere mate, same 'ere – so fuckin' what? We're awl in

the same boat. This'll be my fifth 'oliday this year and I'm off to Bangers in October.'

'What, Wales?'

'No, you prick, fuckin' Wales. Jesus. Bang-fuckin-Kok innit, gonna check out Thailand for three weeks wiv my brutha.'

'Mentalist – how'd you afford that?'

'Flight's a bit pricey but once yer there, live like a king on £5 a day. Luvvly little Thai birds running around for ya all day, fetching drinks, suckin' ya dick, ha ha. Anyway, stop mincing about, you coming or what?'

'Ohhh, I dunno, moving to London soon, not sure if I should.'

'You little gayboy! You tellin' me after last year you're gonna stay home while we're all livin' it large on holiday together?'

I could feel myself getting excited. I knew it'd be a blast, and began trying to justify another trip.

*Hmmmm, got enough money on the card, last chance for all of us to go away together, and, if all goes well, I'll have a job in the city soon.*

'Aaaarg, go on then, I'm in.'

'Good lad, you know it makes sense.'

**8.45 p.m.** I just can't say no anymore. Especially when the company keeps on encouraging me by increasing my limit. It's an invitation to spend, and one I willingly accept.

# Welcome to London – all major cards accepted

*'I do not borrow on credit cards. It is too expensive. I have four young children. I give them advice not to pile up debts on their credit cards.'*

Matt Barrett, CEO of Barclays, addressing the House of Commons Treasury Committee, 2003

Tuesday 1 July, 2003

**6.50 p.m. Bristol: Home**. London calling – with the offer of a job, TWENTY-EIGHT BASTARD GRAND! Kelly was ecstatic when I rang with the news. Everything's falling into place. And I can sleep easy tonight, nothing banishes financial worries like a new salary, ha ha!

Thursday 3 July, 2003

**3.15 p.m. Work**. Big Dave's been on the case with Prague, reply-all emails have been cluttering my inbox all day. Everyone's in and we've got a full compliment.

**3.30 p.m.** Printed off the confirmation page for the six flights I've helpfully booked on my card and the annual foray into Europe is *go*!

Wednesday 23 July, 2003

**10.45 a.m. Bristol: Work**. Posted acceptance form for London position this morning, and handed in my notice. Mr Townsend wasn't surprised. Probably glad to see the back of my slack ways. One month to go before I'm big in the city.

Wednesday 6 August, 2003

**1.24 p.m. Quiet carriage of the Paddington to Bristol Parkway train.**

Need to be kind to myself this week, pushed the boundaries with five booze-soaked days in the Czech Republic. The angry bad-living boil that's erupted on my cheek's a sure sign I've been caning it.

Man, Prague. Have never gone so hard. Pete assumed the role of tour guide, leading us on a five-day circuit of the city's sex establishments. Every time I looked at him he'd be poring over his 'Praha Erotischer Stadtplan,' with its porno cartoon legend and lewd drawings. Our Prague was a city of indecent images and Big Dave has the photos to prove it.

Kelly was understandably apprehensive about the destination, given its reputation as the new sex capital of Europe. I assured her it was just a lads' getaway and that I had no intention of being unfaithful with a hooker when I had a wonderful girlfriend waiting for me at home. 'Besides,' I said. 'I never get a hard-on in those places.'

**1.48 p.m.** The EasyJet-set have landed in Bohemia. The place was crawling with groups of young British men and women. In every square, bar and club, we came across people from home, many on organised tours. Haven't seen that many stags and hens outside of Newquay. God knows what the locals make of it all. Crossing Charles' Bridge en route to our hotel in the small hours after a night in the clubs, we came across a sorry-looking figure who'd been stripped naked, sprayed with metallic graffiti paint, and chained to a statue of St Francis of Assisi. A red T-shirt, emblazoned with 'Rob's Stag Tour '03', had been tied to the plinth below St Francis' feet, the garment flapping in the wind whipping up from the River Vltava below. Big Dave seized the opportunity, pulling out his Cybershot so Ratboy could pose next to the stricken stag for a memento.

**2.15 p.m.** Back in England, five sheepish young bucks are nervously anticipating the bill. Sure, we downed our fair share of the legendary 30p Prague pint, but nobody tells you about the tiny two-gulp cans in the strip clubs at a fiver a go. Those places guzzle money.

For myself and Andy, the only members of the party with serious girlfriends, it was a little absurd to spend so much time drinking in these joints, but we were out-numbered, and the majority ruled. Ratboy and Big Dave kept egging me on to have a private dance, but this time I held firm and didn't buckle under the pressure. It was kind of unnecessary anyway. Everywhere you looked, there were women peeling off their clothes. Every half hour or so, either Ratboy, Pete or Dave would be at the till, swiping their card and disappearing with a girl. Their statements sure will make for interesting reading.

On the subject of statements – major shock when I fed the card into the ATM at Paddington this morning: YOU HAVE INSUFFICIENT FUNDS FOR THIS TRANSACTION.

Huuuuurrrrrgh! Felt that one right in the pit of my stomach. Had been banking on my plastic pal to see me through my first few weeks in London. Like a fool, I also blew all the cash the lads gave me for the flights. As they handed me the money, I knew it wouldn't be going back on the card. Stealing from yourself: financial sleight of hand.

**Wednesday 3 September, 2003**
**11.17 a.m. Office.** Maxed out again, leaving me no option but to call the bank to request an overdraft. Despite my latest blow-out, I'm still flavour of the month with the money men. My application was quickly accepted, with the guy on the phone even suggesting I might want to consolidate my Gold Card balance onto my Graduate Loan. Apparently, they'll pay off my card so it's back to zero, with the balance on the card then added onto my loan. The monthly loan payment will be a touch higher but there's no credit card bill to pay. Something to think about – it'd be nice to see the back of those monthly bills.

Tuesday 9 September, 2003

**9.27 a.m. Bristol: Doormat.** Confirmation of £2,500 overdraft limit. Good news in terms of the big move although I'm back in the red – even on payday. Ah well, no time to dwell on such things… Come Saturday morning, I'll be heading up the motorway to start a new life. It's time to start getting excited. Got lots to do this week: have to pack up all my worldly possessions and say my goodbyes.

**9.45 a.m.** There's also a letter from a loan company I've never heard of, informing me that I've been 'pre-approved' for a five-grand bounty. Just when you think you've run aground, the world is suddenly awash with money again. They've even included a free pen to help me complete the application form.

Thursday 11 September, 2003

**7.45 p.m. Bristol.** My dad rang to see how my moving preparations were coming along, in his own inimitable way of course.

'How's the packing coming along lad, you all set?' he asked jovially.

'Not very well,' I replied, looking around my room despairingly. 'I haven't even started yet.'

'So when am I going to meet this girl who you've turned your life upside down for? What's it she does again, she's a singer isn't she?'

'Yes, she's a singer and you'll meet her soon enough,' I said, immediately growing anxious over Kelly's first encounter with Britain's biggest martyr.

'I remember,' he started, 'when I was about your age. I moved to Doncaster, chasing a girl, a barwoman I met in Christchurch.

Barbara, her name was. She was a singer too, sort of. She was dead cagey about me coming to her gigs, always some excuse why I wasn't allowed to go and see her. So of course I followed her one night. She was a singer alright, but then she'd take all her clothes off. Never been so humiliated in all my life, all those men shouting at my girl like that. You can imagine the things they were saying.' I was trying not to laugh as he finished his story.

'Turns out half the town knew Barbara – *intimately*. Voice of an angel, but the morals of a harlot. Didn't work out of course. Came back down south, wiser and wilier for it.'

'Thanks for that,' I said. 'Very interesting.'

'So why London then, why can't she move to Bristol?' The memory of Barbara had clearly triggered his paternal instincts.

'She's got a lot going on up there,' I said. 'Besides, it's time for a change y'know, keeps life interesting.'

'Well you'll never be able to buy a house if you move to London,' he said sounding his favourite drum. I ignored him this time. I knew he didn't like London much; his view of the place was that it was dirty, smelly and overcrowded.

'Well you could always do it for a bit and then move to Milton Keynes the pair of ya. You'd get more for your money, be able to think about buying a place. And there's plenty to do here, they've just extended the shopping centre, there's loads of new restaurants.'

I pictured the sprawling shopping centre and the mass of cloned chain restaurants, all conveniently grouped together under one roof.

'I can't wait to get to London,' I said emphatically, feeling a twinge of excitement. 'Look, I better get my arse into gear, I've got a lot to do. I'll send you a postcard when I get there.'

### Friday 12 September, 2003

**9.27 a.m. Doormat.** It's worse than I thought. It's ridiculous to go somewhere as cheap as Prague and spend that much. Struggling to recall some of the transactions. So many cash withdrawals – Christ, that looks bad. It can only be a matter of time before somebody at banking HQ sounds the alarm. Expecting them to call anytime soon. Probably be for the best if I'm made to send it back. Hell, it really is like being a junkie, there's no way of stopping unless somebody steps in with the straitjacket and forces you to go cold turkey.

**10.30 a.m.** After this morning's sickener, I've decided I'm through with strip clubs. It's not like I'm trapped in a sexless marriage or in a mid-life crisis. It's stupid to pay £25 to sit with a flaccid cock when I've got a girlfriend at home who'll do almost anything I ask. After all, it's not like I'm with Jim Morrison or Charles Bukowski in a titty bar on the Sunset Strip – more like an IT consultant from Romford and four of his mates sticking their fingers into the arsehole of a bilingual medical student, thanks to a favourable exchange rate.

**10.30 p.m.** Feel sick. Spent the last four hours frantically trying to pack my room up, throwing things into boxes and bin bags and attempting to squash it all into a three-door hatchback. Time for a few goodbye beers with Pete and Jez.

### Saturday 13 September, 2003

**7.30 p.m. London: Kelly's flat.** It's been an emotional day with glassy-eyed farewells to friends and the city that's been my home for seven years. But sentiment went out the window at the end of the M4 as the first towers appeared on the skyline, causing me to erupt in a spontaneous fit of roof-thumping and horn-blowing as I crossed the city limits.

Oh yeah. I'm here for real this time, to set up camp in the world's biggest playground. I've even blagged my way into the girls' dorm, swapping Pete's putrefying trench-foot and Jez's noxious room-clearers for the perfumed aromas of three young women. Ali's fresh out of fashion college and is always looking hot if perhaps a little wacky, and Gemma's a city girl. Both tidy units and good fun.

It's the stuff of fantasies, to be the only male in an all-girl household.

'It'll be like Readers Letters,' I bragged to a very green Pete over a can of Heineken last night, 'y'know, where some student ends up getting a birthday treat from his randy housemates.'

'Bullshit,' he said laughing. 'You'll be *their* bitch. They'll have you wearing nothing but a little pinny, doing all the housework with your skinny white arse hanging out the back.'

Drunken pyjama parties will have to wait as I'm off down the local with the girls to toast my arrival. Have to settle in quickly, I start work on Monday. Feels good to know I'll be living in one single town, a chance to bring some much needed order to my life.

### Sunday 14 September, 2003
**9.30 p.m. Kelly's flat.** Woke up this morning giggling like a couple of kids on Christmas day. We were both too excited to sleep any longer.

'It feels so good having you in my bed, I can't believe you're here,' whispered Kelly into my ear as I opened my eyes, causing me to hug her tightly. 'And you won't be driving home tomorrow.'

I made us breakfast in bed and we sat reading my London city guide, planning all the things we were going to do over the following weeks. First up was Kelly's choice: the London Zoo.

She's obsessed with animals, so we spent the day walking around the enclosures, where she proceeded to bombard me with a mind-boggling array of facts about all kinds of mammals, birds, reptiles and insects. After two hours of continuous trivia, I had to interject. 'I feel like I've spent the day with Terry Nutkins,' I cried. 'My head can't take any more information.'

'Carry on like that and you won't be getting *your* nutkins,' she said with impressive speed, giving my bottom a pinch.

Before we left for home, Kelly turned on the womanly charm and harassed one of the zookeepers into taking a photo of us together by the monkey enclosure. The guy was shaking his head in disbelief as we both posed like primates, clinging to the railings and curling our arms.

**Monday 15 September, 2003**
**6.30 p.m. Home.** Woke up well before the alarm this morning, ready for my first day as a Londoner. Strode to the station at double-quick pace, eager to embark on my commute and get stuck into it. In the ticket hall, I tried to look relaxed, like I'd been doing it for years, but I still wore a massive smile on my face. Giddy with the novelty of the situation, I soaked it all up: the feel of my thin cardboard ticket in my hand, the years of history in the grimy wall tiles, the beeping and clattering barriers, the churn of the escalator, the trump-trump of hundreds of feet, the boarding etiquette on the busy platform, the zap-zap of electricity cracking off the track as the train approached, and the dry smell of metal on metal as it braked to a halt. It was all new and it was all mine. This is a grown-up place, a real city, I thought, as I squeezed into an overcrowded carriage, and already my old life seemed embarrassingly unsophisticated by comparison.

The excitement was briefly tempered by a slight attack of the nerves as I arrived at the office and stepped out of my comfort zone. But by lunchtime I'd calmed down and begun to enjoy it again. Even the first day rituals were different, and the new-boy walk-around resembled a 'meet and greet' of United Nations delegates, a refreshing change from the bland shuffle and muffle with the same old faces. And it's a much younger crowd than I'm used to: shiny slacks and tea-stained ties are the exception here. Around half the office are Antipodean travellers on two-year work visas, mostly big towering Australians with booming voices and bone-crushing handshakes. It's all 'G'day mate' and 'no worries' – like a parody of the weekday soap operas my sister would force me to endure after school. My only slight worry is my new boss, Bettina, a softly-spoken Nigerian lady who talks in a soothing melody and indecipherable accent. I could barely understand a word she said and had to resort to picking out key phrases and nodding politely. Regardless, I think I'm going to like it here – the world in one city and my provincial posterior right in the middle of it.

### Monday 29 September 2003
**6.45 p.m. London: Kelly's flat.** Two weeks in and I'm still skipping along pavements and bounding up escalators – I'm high on life and living the big adventure. Even the novelty of trekking across the city is yet to wear off. I love taking my place amongst the throngs descending into the tunnels and cramming onto packed trains. I even get excited when the name of a stop is announced: 'the next station is… Bank'. Kelly told me I'd be grumbling about it soon.

### Wednesday 1 October, 2003
**7.20 p.m. Home.** Stopped by a bookshop after work. One of my aims for London was to pick up my reading again, something

that's been at the top of my mental 'to do' list for a while now. The new city is a stimulus for change. A man will never flourish within the confines of a group. Now that I'm here, it's time to dispense with some of the old habits and develop some new ones. Read an interesting article on Franz Kafka in the weekend culture section so thought I'd start with him.

### Wednesday 8 October, 2003

**11.02 a.m. Office.** Desperately need to flog the car, haven't had time to sort a resident's permit and it's costing £12.50 a day in loose change. This city sure punishes the absent-minded. Got up late today and some militant parkie had given me a ticket timed at 7.05 a.m. What do they do, camp out in the bushes? Fifty fucking quid as well. I can see why somebody might be inclined to have a pop at one of them.

### Thursday 9 October, 2003

**5.45 p.m. Home.** My jealous old life is trying to interfere with my exciting new one: letter from my previous employers – a bill for £3,500, the outstanding balance of the car loan.

### Saturday 11 October, 2003

**11.45 a.m. Home.** Met Big Dave for a beer last night and received an impromptu lesson in how to juggle thousands of pounds of debt by playing the system and signing up to all the 0% deals. When he opened his wallet to show me his card collection, I felt sure he was involved in some kind of identity fraud scam. It was stuffed full of the things, a brightly coloured assortment of motifs and logos jostling for space. But it's all perfectly legal: according to the article in today's *Metro*, Big Dave's not a 'wide boy', he's a 'rate tart'. Maybe it's time I started making like a credit whore too.

### Monday 13 October, 2003

**9.55 a.m. Work.** Saw an advert on the tube this morning for a credit card with a 0% balance transfer rate (guaranteed for a year). Applied online and was instantly accepted.

### Thursday 16 October, 2003

**11.48 a.m. Office.** Still in the honeymoon period. 'It feels just like being on holiday,' as Kelly described it. Can't disagree with her. We're hardly ever at home. The pace of life here is so different, always something happening, different distractions vying for attention. Of course, the free-spending roller coaster ride continues. It was naïve to think it would be different.

### Friday 17 October, 2003

**2.00 p.m. Office.** It makes me sick. They're laughing at us, the fat cats at the top. Reading the BBC News site over lunch, it says the CEO of Barclays has announced to the House of Commons that he doesn't use credit cards himself, as they're too expensive! The sheer arrogance of the man to come out and brag to the world that his product is a rip-off aimed at mugs. He's warned his kids off them too. I might stop paying the fucker after all. It's too expensive. I wonder if Mr Barrett's little darlings have heeded their father's words. Let's hope not. I mean they print warnings on cigarette packets, but people still smoke.

**6.39 p.m. Home.** Is it a bird, is it a plane – no it's the credit stork arriving with my new singing, dancing 0% EGG card, complete with a £6,000 credit limit.

### Saturday 18 October, 2003

**5.30 p.m.** The degenerates. Phoned Big Dave to see if he and Ratboy fancied a beer in town tonight only to discover that they're otherwise engaged – entertaining a couple of lap dancers from Prague. It appears that they swapped numbers and email addresses with a couple of girls at one of the clubs.

'You're winding me up, how the hell did you sort that out?' I asked Dave, surprised at the audacity of his coup, managing to convince these girls to fly all the way to London.

'Heh-heh,' he sniffed into the phone, 'well, got chatting with two lovelies in one of the booths on the last night, didn't we. The Rat asked them if they'd ever been to London. Should've seen 'em mate, eyes lit up straightaway. Made sure we gave 'em a good tip and promised we'd show 'em a good time. Been on the case sorting it out since we got back,' he said dirtily, his nasal south-east drawl sounding even more blocked up than usual.

'Where are you now?' I asked, still trying to get my head around it.

'I'm waiting for Katerina to finish in the bathroom,' he said smugly, sniffing down the phone again. 'You should see her mate, fit as fuck, right goer 'an all. Shelled out on a King's suite at the Metropole, didn't I. Spent all day on the sniff with her. Ratty's been giving his one a taste of English in the next room. Gotta take them out now, show 'em the sights. Dunno how I'm gonna manage it, I'm absolutely mullered, this shit Ratty got hold of is pure as…' he said explaining the reason for his sniffling.

'Look at you pair, right couple of international playboys,' I said in a state of disbelief, and with a very vivid, seedy image of his hotel room forming in my head.

He was laughing shadily, trying to keep his Czech dancer from hearing him revel in his role as libertine.

'Heh heh, we pay for the flights and hotels and they're our slags for the weekend,' he boasted, very pleased with himself.

'That must've cost you a…'

He cut me off mid-sentence, 'Hang on mate, she's coming back. I'll bell ya tomorrow'.

Well it's one way of seeing the world, I thought, using your clacker as currency. It's that exchange rate at work again. It's fair to say that the European social scene has moved a world away from the time when English gentlemen would return from a summer sojourn to Venice or Monte Carlo, having won the hand of the daughter of a Continental aristocrat. I must be growing up. This is one experience I'm more than happy to live without.

### Monday 20 October, 2003
**10.30 a.m. Office.** Transferred £6,000 from my old card onto the new one to benefit from a 12-month interest-free holiday. Have to refrain from using the Gold Card now. If I run that back up to the limit, I'm in serious trouble.

### Friday 24 October, 2003
**10.15 a.m. Work.** Received a rather unfriendly reminder about the car loan. Expected better from a public organisation, but their letter made it abundantly clear that I'd have the debt collectors on my tail if I went on ignoring them. Had no choice but to pay it off with the Gold Card.

**11.30 a.m.** It's a day of letters. This one's so good, I've pinned it up by my desk. It's from an irate member of the public, pleading for reason from the Council. So exasperated is the author of this missive that he actually signed off by asking 'whether we were familiar with the works of Franz Kafka'. Picked up the poor bugger's file and found a succession of requests for information, all of which had been duly complied with, only to be followed by further demands for previously unasked-for documentation. Having recently become *au fait* with the trials of Joseph K, I can certainly sympathise. Tempted to address the reply 'Dear Joseph K'. Joke's on me though – after all, I'm part of the same machine.

### Monday 3 November, 2003
**11.15 p.m. London.** My status as 'man of the house' has been disturbed. Kelly's housemate, Gemma, has her boyfriend, Zach, crashing here whilst he's between flats. He arrived, along with his snowboard, at the weekend.

Loud, assertive and dominant, Zach's the kind of person who's impossible to ignore. He makes it his business to fill a room with his massive personality until everybody else is gasping for air. His confidence is quite understandable: he was certainly dealt a good hand in the genetic lottery. Broad-shouldered and dark, as well as being handsome in a plain, unblemished way, not to mention quick-witted, Zach is what most people would describe as *a model of good breeding*.

But being in his company is wearying. Everything he says, does or talks about is tinged with an air of competitiveness – the kind that's in the DNA of every successful public schoolboy, his combative edge sharpened to a point from having spent his formative years surrounded by equally win-hungry rivals. If you've got a story, he's got a better one. There's nothing the man cannot do or hasn't done. He and Gemma are both into extreme sports and shirk no test of their bravery. They've even got a favourite phrase, 'wicked pace', which they repeat to one another at every opportunity. I have to chew my knuckles every time I hear it. And when he's not throwing himself off a cliff or out of a plane, his travel tales are marked by a kind of Sunday magazine exclusiveness, involving esoteric destinations of the 'did it years before the masses caught on' type.

And the man doesn't know the meaning of relaxation; he can't go out for a civilised drink without turning it into some sort of chest-thumping bravado session. Pints have to be followed by shots, 'eating's cheating' and all that tedious shit. He had me pinned to the bar in the pub earlier for a bit of male bonding while the girls were busy chatting. He told me he worked in Mayfair, managing funds or something.

'You're a public sector boy aren't you?' he said scornfully.

I nodded sheepishly.

'Working for the government – first sign of defeat eh?' he said, elbowing me in the arm to signal it was merely sport. One thing about Zach, he's not the type to care if he's just met you; he'll still go straight in for the kill.

'All day drinking tea and home at three o'clock to feed the cat,' he continued, 'you skivers are dining out on my taxes. That's why I went offshore – so you lazy fuckers can't waste it!' He then guffawed and tipped his fat head back and laughed at his own joke.

**Thursday 6 November, 2003**
**10.25 a.m. Work.** Walked to the tube station with Zach this morning. As we negotiated packed pavements and crossed busy roads, he barely looked up from fiddling with his *Blackberry* device. It's never out of his reach and he spends all night tapping away on it.

The twat also did a little set piece when he left me to change trains at Oxford Circus. He spun around on the platform as the doors were closing, amidst the surge of people pushing to get on, threw a double-handed point at me like some sort of motivation coach and yelled 'it's all about the money'. He's like Jerry Maguire without the heart.

**Friday 14 November, 2003**
**9.30 p.m. Home.** Rick and Abby came down to London this week, for a mix of business and pleasure. It's been over a year since I saw them. It's what happens as you get older, people's lives veer off in different directions and occasions for coming together become less frequent.

Rick was late for our lunchtime rendezvous in Covent Garden, because he was held up at work. I met Abby at the Boulevard Bar and Brasserie, at a table surrounded by boutique bags. She looked the part, wearing a full-length fitted leather coat and leather boots. She'd had her hair done too, by the look of things.

'What's taking him so long?' I asked Abby after the salutations, as we ordered aperitifs.

'Oh, it's their bloody annual conference this week. Rick had to give a speech yesterday. The directors were really impressed with him and he got invited to their breakfast meeting this morning.'

'Breakfast with the directors,' I said, nodding my head.

'Yeah, he's on course for being made a partner next year,' she said, sounding slightly unenthusiastic.

'Isn't that what he wanted?' I questioned, picking up on her half-hearted endorsement of his progress.

'Yeah of course, don't get me wrong we both want it. But…' she hesitated. 'It's the hours… *I never see him!*' She looked at me like she was appealing to me for help.

She looked upset, they'd obviously planned to spend the day together and Abby'd been left to her own devices. Hence the multitude of shopping bags. She dabbed her eye with a napkin and I tried to think of something to say.

'You guys should book a holiday,' I offered feebly, aware of the rank inadequacy of my suggestion.

'We're going skiing at Christmas,' she said shakily, trying to stop herself from crying.

'You made any plans for the wedding yet?' I enquired, hoping this hadn't become a sore subject.

'Oh yeah, we've almost set a date,' she said, her eyes lighting up. 'It'll definitely be next year, I've made him promise.'

Abby's phone rang. It was Rick, he was two minutes away. Instinctively we both reached for the menus. When Rick arrived, Abby was a different person. Obviously, she just wanted her man by her side. They held hands almost the entire time. Watching them together as we ate and updated each other on our lives, I thought how very much in love they still were. Admirable given how many years they'd been together.

We spent the afternoon enjoying lunch as it should be – long and leisurely. Afterwards, I walked them to the theatre where they had tickets for a show, then caught the tube to Kentish Town to meet Kelly after work.

'I don't ever want you to work like that,' she said after I'd told her about my day. 'I don't care if you're poor, I just want us to be happy.'

'You don't have to worry about that,' I laughed. 'Remember who you're talking to. I haven't got it in me. Y'know, I feel like I work too much already, and I only do regular hours. Although it's not so much the hours, more *what* I do. I don't want to be doing this shit for the rest of my life,' I griped, sounding slightly bitter.

'No, it's not really you, is it,' she said agreeing.

I'd surprised myself, voicing these thoughts for the first time. Until now it's all been a bit of a game. I've given little thought to the choices I've made, kind of aimlessly bumbling along. Maybe living in the city and mixing with all the different people I've met, I've started to see another side to life and begun to question my own.

'Well, I'm glad you've got faith in me,' I said, grateful that she too didn't see me rattling around the fusty corridors of the Town Hall till I retired.

As Kelly went up to the bar I reflected on the significance of my life choices, particularly my abandoned philosophy course, foolishly jettisoned all those years ago in favour of a vocational path. Ah, the vocational degree... No more than a glorified work-training programme, churning out report-writers and masters of the bullet point for the modern workplace.

### Sunday 28 November, 2003
**3.30 p.m. Home.** I'm not going out to dinner with those clowns again. Got dragged out for Gemma's birthday with her, Zach and the banking crowd. Those guys may tread the same pavement as the rest of us but they live in a different world. Having endured two hours of strained conversation with a herd of lairy dickheads it came to settling up. Myself and Kelly were itching to pay the bill and get the hell out of there. Then this guy Rupert pipes up, a plummy twat with a deep tan, wearing a lemon-coloured Ralph Lauren polo shirt.

'C'mon chaps, you know the drill, cards in the middle.'

Without hesitating, everyone threw their cards in, but instead of handing them to the waiter, Rupert hauled Gemma up from her seat and blindfolded her with a napkin.

'Birthday girl does the honours,' he said, guffawing and steering her hand towards the table.

'What's he doing?,' I asked the buffoon on my left. I caught Zach at the other end of the table observing my bewilderment and wearing an amused grin as the guy explained.

'Huh-huh,' he snorted with an air of satisfaction at my ignorance, 'you telling me you never played credit card roulette before, ole chap?'

*Whaaaat!*

An explanation wasn't necessary, although I got one anyway,

'Loser foots the bill – better cross your fingers!' he said, smiling broadly and sweeping his hair back revealing a disgustingly large *Tag Heuer* clamped to his wrist.

There were about twenty people at the table and the wine had been flowing. I tried to do a quick calculation, but before I could finish my sums Gemma had handed the not-so-lucky card to ringmaster Rupert.


'DRUM-ROLL PER-LEASE!'


His cronies, obviously well-drilled, immediately gathered their cutlery, which they hammered on the table to a crescendo. The other customers were all looking over, wondering what all the commotion was about.

'And the winner is… Mr Joshua Jarvis!'

I breathed a huge sigh of relief, although Kelly had been oblivious to the whole thing.

'What's going on?' she said perplexed.

'I'll tell you later,' I said wearily, 'get your coat.'

As we stood up to leave, Joshua Jarvis, a big rugby player type with comically large teeth, was being goaded by his chums as he sportingly signed for the bill.

### Sunday 7 December, 2003
**1.30 p.m. Home.** Another blow-out. Pete and Ratboy's big farewell bash last night in the West End. In a few hours they'll be nursing their hangovers on a plane to Thailand.

### Monday 9 December 2003
**3.25 p.m. Work.** Discovered a great second-hand bookstore close to the office. The portly gentleman who runs the place greeted me with a wonderfully operatic 'good afternoon', and sat humming along to his symphony as he sifted through a box of new arrivals. Stayed so long I gave myself a neck-ache. At least work can't monitor my browsing time. Only worry is being sprung leaving the shop with a bundle tucked under my arm.

### Thursday 11 December, 2003
**11.15 a.m. London: Office.** Took a call from the bank: 'a health check' according to the bloke who rang me. He asked me if I was happy with the service I was receiving and whether there was anything they could do for me?

'Nothing, everything's fine,' I replied.

'Have you thought about consolidating your credit card balance into your graduate loan?' he offered helpfully. 'You'd be paying less interest that way.'

I couldn't see the harm in this. In fact, it sounded entirely logical, although his interest in my welfare seemed a little unusual. I agreed to shift the balance of the Gold Card onto my

Graduate Loan, and he arranged to pay off my overdraft and move that into my loan as well. The monthly loan payment won't actually increase a great deal, partly because it's structured over the longest possible terms (nine years) and, psychologically, I'd prefer to be in the black on payday.

I'm getting good at this. All I have to do is pop into my local branch this afternoon to sign the new agreement. And every new bank loan has a silver lining in the form of a one-month payment break before it kicks into gear. That'll help cushion the cost of Christmas.

**2.25 p.m. Office.** Hmmmm, that didn't feel so good. The bout of banter with the guy from the bank initially dulled my senses. All that excitable football chatter made me feel like I was buying a pound of spuds from an East End barrow boy rather than signing up to a near decade-long loan.

The branch supervisor who dealt with me was far younger than any I've previously encountered: a chap about my age who introduced himself as Darren Chatterton, as he crushed my fingers with his ludicrously firm handshake. 'Daz', as he insisted I call him as we sat down to do business, was a proper Essex boy with the fashion sense of a Premiership footballer, wearing a well-pressed bright pink shirt with a white tie, and sporting a heavily-gelled spiky haircut. Daz was cocksure and full of blather, the type of person who refuses to allow silence or pauses in conversation. He didn't stop jabbering, asking me all kinds of questions at machine-gun speed, matching each of my answers with stories about himself. His angle was that he was everybody's mate, the kind of salesperson whose trick is to quickly assess what kind of person he's dealing with, and then try and find out something about them to latch onto. His team was West Ham, mine Aston Villa: 'ah y'see claret and blue geez, I knew you were alright'. Yes, both our teams wore the same colour strip, so we had a connection, a very tenuous connection.

After just ten minutes I was exhausted, but had still provided him with enough information to process my new loan and write my biography. He was harmless though, even funny in places. I couldn't help laugh when he inappropriately revealed how he'd been sent off whilst playing for his team last weekend for calling the ref 'a fat, cheating slap-head'.

Despite the ear-bullying, I was overcome by a real sense of unease as I signed my name, committing myself to a nine-year loan, a feeling I've been unable to shake ever since. Have been trying to derive comfort from the knowledge that I'm not unique in all this, almost everyone I know has cards and loans these days. Of course, I've no intention of allowing it to run until I'm 36. Perish the thought. I'm telling myself it's the sensible thing to do for now, keep the payments low until I'm earning the really big bucks.

# Leisure & Tourism

*'Sometimes it's nice to have second helpings. And if you've got a lot on your plate, like unexpected bills, credit card bills or overdrafts - or you'd just like a break away from it all, then a top-up to your current Egg loan could be the answer.'*

Promotional literature from EGG

## Thursday 1 January, 2004

**8.30 p.m. London: Home.** Ahhhh the relief. Nothing quite like the sight of your own front door after the intensity of family duty over Christmas. Discounting freak tsunamis, I can see why Pete and Ratboy would choose to spend it on a beach in Thailand instead of being cooped up with their relatives in front of the TV. Unfortunately, Mum's Christmas buffet coincided with the final of *Pop Idol*. I'm not sure which is worse, the theatrical blubbering of the starry-eyed fame wannabes pleading with the nation to vote for them, or the very real tears of my aunty Janice who completely falls for the whole tiresome charade.

My visit to the old man's house almost passed without incident. Except for that bloody programme, *To Buy or not To Buy*, or maybe it was *Homes Under the Hammer* – one of those property porn TV shows – that lit the fuse. Familiar story: cameras following a successful middle class couple who'd quit their jobs to become property developers. It was real edge-of-the-seat stuff as the couple's renovation budget dwindled, threatening to eat into their profit margin. Did they really need to spend so much on bathroom fixtures? After all, as the presenter had to keep reminding them, 'you're not going to be living in it yourselves'. Luckily, Giles and Hannah came to their senses and, with some wily readjustments, managed to turn a profit.

I'd held my tongue for the duration – it was the season of goodwill after all – but my dad just couldn't help himself:

'Y'know your cousin Mike's just bought himself a place on buy-to-let in Bletchley.'

*Friggin Bletchley… If Milton Keynes is the arsehole of Britain, then Bletchley's a smelly little wingnut clinging to the rectal ring-road.*

'That's nice for him,' I said, trying to hide my contempt. I could picture it all too easily: gormless little Mike and his dull fiancée, brochures in hand, spending their Saturdays trudging around a sink estate after some spiky-haired bell-end in a Mini. 'Aye, putting his money into bricks 'n' mortar, you wanna take a leaf outta his book.'

'There's plenty of time for that, Dad. I'm just enjoying myself. You only get one life y'know.'

'That's all well and good, but what'll you have when your older eh? Y'wanna start taking life seriously, son. You should be saving some of it instead of gallivanting around the world all the time,' he said, clearly referring to my spate of breaks. 'Y'know he's a sensible lad, your cousin,' he remarked, full of admiration, and making no attempt to disguise his disappointment at how I'd turned out.

Dad's always loved little Mike. He left school at sixteen and followed his father and uncle into the family business, learnt his trade and recently set up on his own.

'*Another working class hero in the making*,' I muttered under my breath, thinking aloud.

'What was that?'

I was about to change the subject but something inside me snapped.

'Oh for god's sake, Mike's a fucking deadshit. He's never left Buckinghamshire, let alone England. And another thing, I'm not screwing myself in the arse just so I can buy some filthy little grot box in the middle of a war zone. There's more to life y'know.'

I hadn't meant to unleash such a foul-mouthed tirade, but I'd been provoked. Thankfully, Kelly was in the conservatory, being subjected to the family photograph album by Jan. An uneasy silence filled the room. For the first time in my life, I'd rendered him speechless. I cracked open a can of beer and took a long guzzle. Being a builder, his obsession with property is understandable – me and my sister were being dragged around the *Ideal Homes* exhibition long before the white collar masses began deserting their desks for a slice of the action. Sundays were often spent trudging after him down the aisles of B&Q, MFI and Homebase, where we amused ourselves playing housey in all the showrooms. By the time I had hair on my balls, I'd seen enough of that world.

'What do you do with all your money anyway?' he said, resuming the offensive. It takes more than a few profanities to deter the old fella. 'You're on a good whack now, y'got any saved?'

I gave him a look. He knew damn well I never saved a penny.

'And what's that bloody credit card doing in your wallet? You think I didn't notice that, eh? You should steer well clear, you'd do well to cut that thing up right now. Y'know in my day we never had 'em, good thing too. You wanted something then, y'had to save for it first. And y'know what, eh? By the time you'd saved up, y'realised you didn't want whatever it was in the first place.'

My blood went cold. *If only you knew,* I thought to myself. *That little card's just the tip of the iceberg…*

It was clearly time to beat a retreat. He was more than welcome to the last word. Luckily, he left it there. I had to admit he was right about the debt thing. Dad's got a pathological fear of debt aside from the sacred mortgage. He runs an extremely tight ship and never owes anybody anything. I wish I'd lived in an age before credit cards and loans. I'm sure things were a lot simpler then. Thinking of a New Year's resolution isn't difficult, sticking to it'll be the hard part.

## Monday 5 January, 2004

**10.00 a.m. Office.** Happy New Year! Woke to the shrill of the alarm with a sore throat, and had to drag myself through the rain, spitting germs onto the pavement, arriving at the tube station, wet and shivering. A large filthy brown puddle had formed outside the entrance to welcome returning commuters.

The combination of the weather and the time of year made for a particularly unpleasant journey: dank carriages crammed with sweaty bodies hurtling through dark tunnels, the drawn faces of reluctant nine-to-fivers glumly turning the pages of the *Metro* or staring blankly into space in a white headphone trance. Cynically timed advertisements pasted to the walls offered the antidote to the city: tablets to combat fatigue and raise energy levels, posters pedalling pills to prevent colds alongside instructions from a budget airline to 'Take the Piccadilly Line to Heathrow'.

**11.45 a.m.** Spent an hour surfing the net for cheap city breaks in a bid to lift the gloom.

**3.45 p.m. Office.** Meeting room hell. A two-hour bore fest with every drone having their say on the scintillating subject of *Best Value Performance Indicators*. Feel like I've just gone twelve rounds with Tyson – my mind's turned to sludge. It never ceases to confound me, how people can manage to talk so much shit for so long. Considering the lifelessness of the subject, the levels of enthusiasm displayed are perverse. But I find it impossible to follow the discussion and always pass the time with a spot of daydreaming, usually involving a speculative analysis of the sex lives of my colleagues. By the end of the first hour, I've normally mind-fucked every passable female in the room. But even that can only amuse me for so long, and I soon get sick of my own thoughts. There's nowhere to run to and you're locked in. After a time I can feel myself slipping mentally, like I'm splitting or cracking. Sometimes I get all panicky that I'm about to have a Tourette's moment and might bark out a random obscenity. It's not a natural environment – in fact it's exceedingly unnatural. Surely I can't be the only one thinking like this? There must be others in that room that feel the same way, like-minded souls that also struggle with the falseness and abnormality of the situation? I'm not so sure. I scan the faces and hear the belief in their voices and feel horribly isolated.

### Saturday 10 January, 2004

**11.30 a.m. Home.** Zach's finally moving out. He and one of his cohorts have bought a place close to Hyde Park. I was more than happy to help them load the van up and send him on his way. As I handed him his snowboard he took it as a cue to begin a bout of bragging.

'Man, I don't lose out on travel. You gotta enjoy it, haven't you? Last year was a big one for me with holidays; snowboarding twice, France then Canada, a two week tour of Argentina, four weeks in the Far East, although that was mainly business, then Monaco for the Grand Prix.' He was in a boisterous mood and his voice boomed and reverberated off the hollow walls of the box van.

'Hey, did Gemma tell you we're going to Cuba for a weekend?' he bellowed from inside the container, treading so heavily that the vehicle bounced up and down. 'When that Communist fucker carks it, the place'll open right up. It'll be time for those bean-eating Spics to say hello to the Free Market!'

'You're going to Cuba for a weekend – all that way for a few nights?'

'Don't give me that environmental shit,' he said bullishly, clumping forward to stand on the tail lift with his arms outstretched, 'I couldn't give a fuck about a bit of melting ice.'

'No more snowboarding though, right?' I said looking up at him on his platform.

'Nah. It's all bollocks anyway. Even if it is true, either I won't be around to see it or, if the shit does come crashing down and a few Indians are being washed out to sea, then I'll have enough money to be on the right side of it. Whatever storm may come.'

After they'd gone I went back inside to clear the lounge of packing debris. Amongst the bubble wrap and bits of cardboard, I found a loose photograph on the floor. I turned it over to be greeted by the sight of Zach and his chums in a group pose, standing in all their snow gear on a mountain. Maybe Zach's right I thought, maybe it is all about the money. He'll certainly have a full life to look back on and there's no second act. I was still holding the picture as I considered his approach to existence. I thought about the way some people travel, pounding around the world from destination to destination, with no real purpose other than superficial box-ticking. Then I spotted something I hadn't noticed before – one of Zach's buddies stood behind him on a rock and had unzipped himself to place his penis on the shoulder of his unsuspecting friend. It made me smile for a moment, before I realised that I was laughing *with* them. Irked, I binned the photo and headed out for breakfast.

### Thursday 29 January, 2004

**11.25 a.m. Office.** Cheeky bastards timed that deliberately. Pete and Ratboy called from their mountain retreat in Thailand after a day riding motorbikes through remote jungle. The Rat gleefully remarked that the sound of the office in the background was like music to his ears. I'd imagine anything would sound tuneful when you're smoking opium reefers several thousand metres above sea level.

**11.45 a.m.** Checked out their *Yahoo!* photo album, a braggers' blog set up to show everyone back home what a good time they're having. Managed to look at about two pics before closing it down, the sight of their smiling sunburnt faces too much to bear under the glare of the office striplights in the thick of winter. They've both shaved their heads and are sporting the obligatory 'crazy traveller haircut'. Hate to admit it, but I'm jealous. There's no chance of me downing tools and heading off into the sun like that, not with my level of commitment.

**2.00 p.m.** Spent a brooding lunch in the café by myself reading Kerouac's 'On The Road'. Sal Paradise and Dean Moriarty criss-crossing America: freedom and kicks – not a swipe card between them.

**3.00 p.m.** A tonic to lift my spirits in the form of another flight itinerary, hot off the office printer. Berlin this time, booked for next month.

**1.00 a.m. Home.** When you're feeling a bit down and want to be left to brood in peace, the intuitive sixth sense of women is often at its sharpest. I'd been fairly quiet all evening and Kelly could sense something was up.

'You want to be with your friends, don't you? You've had enough of me and I'm keeping you trapped here,' she said as we climbed into bed. Earlier I'd told her about my morning update from Asia.

'Not at all. I moved up here because I wanted to be with you,' I said truthfully.

'If you want to go, tell me now, I don't want you stringing me along and then deciding it's not what you want,' she said unconvinced by my response, grabbing the duvet and turning to the wall so I couldn't see her face.

I moved up to her from behind and wrapped my arms around her but she was tense and stiff.

'It's just difficult,' I said, rolling back. 'I'm watching them follow their dreams.'

'You've never said you wanted to go travelling,' she said, anxiously through the muffle of the duvet, still facing the wall.

'That's not it,' I said sitting up and drawing my knees to my chest. 'I've got so much debt, I can't think about doing anything different with my life until I've paid it off. That call today brought it home to me, that's all.'

She turned back around, still hoarding all the covers.

'Okay,' she said softly, sounding almost convinced. She wore a vulnerable expression, her eyes were wide and misty. 'It's just that you're normally so happy, I get scared when you go into yourself.'

She reached out a hand and smoothed my arm.

'Aren't you cold?' she asked, noticing the goosebumps that appeared on my arms.

'Freezing,' I chattered. 'You look like a bloody Eskimo wrapped up like that, let me in will ya.'

She dropped off to sleep in just a few minutes like she always did. When I've something on my mind, I can lie awake for hours. After a while, I got up and rolled a cigarette, opening one of the attic roof-lights to stand with my head out, smoking and staring into the orange-tinged sky. Something had been nagging at me of late. I'd settled into the city, but it had caused me to become unsettled in another way. There had to be something more, something other than offices, paydays, pubs and holidays. There's a rhythm to life, but for most people it's a monotonous one. The best lives are those where the beat is unpredictable and constantly changes.

### Sunday 1 February, 2004
**10.30 a.m. Home.** Kelly sprang a fantastic birthday surprise for me. It's possibly the most thoughtful gift anyone's ever given me: a 12-week creative writing course at Islington College. Looks like she's been paying attention to all my grumbling.

### Tuesday 16 March, 2004
**8.30 p.m. Home.** Have begun looking for a place with Kelly. Had no qualms about the decision either. That's one area of my life that seems to be heading in the right direction.

### Wednesday 17 March, 2004
**10.00 p.m. Home.** Attended my first evening class. Utterly inspirational to be among such interesting people. Did feel somewhat like an impostor though, most of them were working on novels or screenplays. I can hardly ask the tutor to appraise my collection of sex stories. Or maybe I should? I might be able to land a job working on one of the top shelf magazines. I'd take that any day over being the public face of the Council.

### Monday 22 March, 2004
**8.30 p.m. Home.** Found ourselves a flat in Stoke Newington. Being the only one with access to funds, had to stump up over a grand in deposit and agency fees (one more to the Gold Card).

Kelly's been maxed out for months, those bloody store cards are the worst – she's been juggling the blasted things for years, only paying off the interest. She has nowhere near my level of commitment, but in proportion to her 20K secretarial salary, she can't take on any more. We've talked about it a few times, how we'd both be well set up if neither of us had any debts to pay.

Still, it was a nice moment walking away from the letting agent's with the rental contract tucked under my arm and Kelly hanging closely on the other, as we headed to the nearest pub to toast our first home together. Although, unbeknownst to Kelly, my happiness was tempered by a sense of impending doom as I silently fretted over another huge outlay appearing on my next statement. As we talked enthusiastically about the big move, our faces glowing from the heat of the roaring fireplace next to our table, I kept thinking about how much it was all costing: the deposit, agency fees, first month's rent, van hire, the furniture we didn't have for our unfurnished flat. Not wanting to spoil the mood as Kelly excitedly planned a trip to IKEA, I guzzled my way towards the two-pint mark – one's troubles usually receded once the first pair had worked their magic. As Kelly made her way to the bar for another round, I sat staring out of the window at the busy street lined with restaurants, bars and café tables. It was a nice area. We had friends around here. I stretched my legs out, resting my feet on the hearth, and began to feel warm and contented as I looked forward to assuming our position as *Popular Local Couple*.

### Saturday 27 March, 2004

**3.30 p.m. Home.** I really am bored of the weekend pub scene: banks of men passively watching some sporting contest on a giant screen. Decided I'd stay indoors and put pen to paper to produce something to take to the writing class. At least the premise for my short story might give the tutor a chuckle; it's based on an evolutionary quirk that's resulted in homosexual men being able to father children. The inspiration came from one of the managers at work, a gay guy who's a dead ringer for Jimmy Somerville from the Communards, and who insists on loudly discussing his nocturnal antics within earshot of half the office.

### Saturday 3 April, 2004

**7.00 p.m. Home.** Moved into our new one-bedroom love palace yesterday: a first floor flat with wooden floors throughout. Managed to kit the place out with a combination of parental donations and a rather costly trip to Argos.

It felt great loading all of our things into a van together and driving across the city to set up home. Kelly's already tested the bathroom for acoustics. I filled the tub for her first bath while she was out at the shop, lit candles around the room and brought her a glass of champagne as she soaked and sang.

**9.30 p.m.** Kelly's put her stamp on our new home already. Walked into the lounge to see our Monkey Magic photo from London Zoo blown up and framed, sitting in the middle of the mantelpiece. 'We look ridiculous, like a couple of lunatics,' I said chuckling, 'it's us who should be locked in a cage.'

**11.45 p.m.** 'Ohhh you're making me come.' Have just heard the couple downstairs having sex. Earlier this afternoon I swear I heard the bloke fart. City living.

Am yet to actually set eyes on them but already feel acquainted.

**Sunday 4 April, 2004**

**1.00 p.m. Home.** Frolicked the morning away in our new super king-size bed, letting our neighbour know that a virile young couple had taken possession of the penthouse.

**Monday 12 April, 2004**

**12.30 p.m. Office.** 'Toss-pot!' Rick calling.

'Alright fella, to what do I owe…'

'Mate, news update, have to be brief, got an appointment in five,' he barked down the phone like he was on the floor of the stock exchange.

'Fire away,' I said.

'Two things. One, we've finally set a wedding date for September, details to follow,' he said followed by a loud crunching sound.

'Are you eating?'

'Apple,' he said impatiently, annoyed at the interruption and still chomping, 'this is my lunch break. Anyway, pay attention you student twat. The second piece of news is that Austen's sorted out the stag for June, just checking your availability for the weekend of the 12th?'

'Sounds fine, where is it?'

'Ahhh, you'll like this,' he said laughing, 'fucking Poland.'

'Poland? Why… Oh hang on, you're not still on the trail of that cleaning company are you? Let it go mate.'

'Good one. No. This was Austen's call. The good news is that it's six Polish Zloty to the Pound so it'll be cheaper than anything we can do at home. We'll be serious players over there with that kind of exchange rate and Aus said there's loads of mental activities. Anyway, time's up, gotta dash. Aus'll send through the details and then JFD.'

'JFD?'

'Just Fucking Do it. Get it booked son. I'll give you a proper call when I'm less busy, adios.'

**4.30 p.m.** Details for Poland came through and I'm booked to go, although this could well be the last of such trips for a while – finances ain't too good.

### Tuesday 20 April, 2004

**4.25 p.m. Office.** Nipped into the jolly hummer's bookshop on the way back from a site visit. Whenever I'm out on business, the lure of the sagging shelves is impossible to resist. The perfect way to grow your library on a budget.

### Friday 23 April, 2004

**9.55 a.m. Office.** Shit. The noose seems to have tightened rather suddenly. I'm being slowly strangled by a complex knot of direct debits and minimum payments, leaving me little breathing space. Only got paid a week ago and already need to be careful.

**10.30 a.m.** It's occurred to me that I don't actually know how much I owe. Not sure I want to.

**1.30 a.m.** Trouble sleeping due to money worries. Did some sums earlier and spent the rest of the evening fretting about the amount I'm liable for. I should've hit the brakes months ago and now it's too late. It feels like a bad dream, only there's no waking up from it.

The numbers are so ridiculous it's easy to believe that they aren't real, like they belong to somebody else. As I lay in bed, fidgeting restlessly, turning everything over in my head I began thinking about the abstract nature of money. On one hand it *isn't* real, it's a man-made concept. It only exists if you believe in it. In which case, all I need do is close my eyes and refuse to recognise it. I'll simply write to my creditors to inform them of my new metaphysical position and I'll be a free man again. Right. It says something when crackpot theories represent your only viable solution. Time to break out the brandy if I'm to get any shuteye.

**Saturday 1 May 2004**
**3.49 p.m. Back in Bristol.** *'Dear Mr Livingson,*
*You have been pre-approved for a personal loan of...'*

Sitting at the kitchen table in my old house with a huge pile of post that Jez's been saving for me. There must be at least twenty letters here, all from various card and loan companies offering me money.

*'Dear Mr Livingson,*
*Don't waste a second, return these forms and you could get your hands on...'*

Looks like I've struck plastic gold. If I were to return all of them I could easily 'get my hands on' over £100,000. That's one solution to my current predicament: damn it all and plunge headlong into oblivion, live the next few years in unimaginable luxury. We could start by joining the boys in Thailand. Tried to get a rise out of Jez telling him I planned to take all the money and disappear into the jungle to live out our days as the King and Queen of Credit. Worryingly, he almost believed me. It's tempting though, it'd sure make for one hell of a story.

*'Dear Mr Livingson,*
*You're only one step away from…'*

## Wednesday 5 May, 2004

**9.25 a.m. Office.** Bit washed out this morning. Suffering from a bad bout of heartburn after too many late-night cigarettes and my eyes feel itchy and sore. Spent countless minutes lying awake last night staring into the blackness, growing ever more frustrated at the sound of Kelly's untroubled snoozing. At night, one is alone with one's thoughts and mine turned to unsettling visions of financial apocalypse. In my semi-conscious state I played out the panic-inducing scenario that all of my creditors would simultaneously call in their loans, demanding immediate payment in full. Before I'd made the sensible decision to get up and have a cognac and cigarette, I'd imagined a full nightmare of urgent threatening letters, bailiffs breaking down the door, desperate pleas to my father, eviction and homelessness, all ending with a horrible Kafkaesque court appearance. I was relieved to finally get to sleep and wake up to the calm order of day, where night sweats and wild charging thoughts seem daft and irrational. Still feel knackered though. Wish they'd provide a room at work where you could bunk down for half an hour.

## Monday 10 May 2004

**3.29 p.m. Office.** If the good times are coming to an end, then I may as well have one final blowout. In a fit of illogical and impulsive madness, I've just booked two foolhardy weeks in Croatia. It hasn't helped that the Antipodean contingent have been chattering incessantly about their summer holiday plans for what seems like weeks. Inca trails and month-long tours of Europe seem to be in vogue this year – it's impossible to avoid getting caught up in it. Engage anyone in a conversation about travel and witness their demeanour change instantly. Faces brighten, eyes sparkle, memories of previous experiences are recounted with a romanticised yearning, whilst future plans are explained with an infectious vibrancy stimulated by the promise of adventure and discovery. Rather stupidly, I also allowed myself to be hoodwinked by a sense of entitlement. After all, I reasoned, ignoring my financial predicament, I'm in the same job as these guys. This is the last one though. It is very definitely the last. Planning to start in the north and drive the coastal road down towards Dubrovnik.

### Wednesday 12 May, 2004

**2.30 p.m. Work.** I never thought I'd agree with Zach on anything, but having sat through our latest monthly meeting, he does have a point about the public sector. We had to endure an hour-long presentation from the new 'Corporate Projects and Performance Coordinator', a young Indian woman dressed in a sharp and pricey looking trouser suit.

As I sat listening to this exuberant little butterfly talk animatedly about 'cross-departmental synergies' and 'corporate partnerships', I found myself zoning out again and coming over a little light-headed. As she pulverised the English language with her unintelligible twaddle, her sidekick, a handsome Canadian guy in his twenties with tightly cropped hair and shiny cufflinks on his wrists, fiddled with a fancy laptop projector showing us all sorts of elaborate flowcharts and key words set to bullet-points. Rather than providing clarification, these 'visual aids' only assisted in adding to my confusion.

As the bombardment reached the half-hour mark I began to experience the onset of a splitting sensation in my forehead. By the end I couldn't focus properly. All I could think was that these two puppets are probably picking up 30K a year each to peddle this nonsense (as well as pay for their expensive clothes). The only redemption came at the end, when the request for post-presentation questions was met with a blank and stupefied silence.

**Monday 14 June, 2004**
**11.00 a.m. Office.** Returned from Rick's stag-do in the early hours. Got to work incredibly tired but glad to be home and no longer associated with the boorish behaviour of my compatriots.

Our group comprised an unlikely mix of old school friends and a few of Rick's work colleagues. Two of which, Mark and Jason, both in their mid-twenties and married with kids, clearly saw this trip as an opportunity to indulge in as much extra-marital sex as possible. They behaved like zoo animals let out of their cage for rutting season, spending each night with prostitutes from the clubs and justifying their infidelity with the tiresome rugby club mantra of 'what goes on tour stays on tour'. Rick, to be fair to him, looked extremely uncomfortable during his romp with the 'Babes in Oil' at the strip joint on Saturday night. After watching the girls wrestle and writhe in the greasy plastic lube pit, the stag was required to jump into the ring, wearing just his pants, the objective being to try and remove the girls' bikinis before they stripped him naked. They'd probably never encountered such reluctance, to the great disappointment of Mark and Jason who were filming the bout on their phones.

Speaking with one of the girls who worked the tables in the club, I learnt that almost all their customers were English. It was this local thirst for tourist cash and the relative poverty of the country that gave its Anglo-Saxon visitors licence to behave with such rampant impunity. Although not all of Krakow welcomed us with open legs: one bar we walked past had a sign on the door which read, 'No British Groups'.

On Sunday, fatigued with all the hyperactivity and empty-headed titillation, myself and Chris, whom I knew vaguely from school and who'd studied history at Cambridge, decided to take a taxi to the Auschwitz concentration camp museum, an hour's drive from Krakow. Chris was a sensitive chap, with a pleasant, soft manner. Following an interesting discussion on the history of Europe and the Second World War, he confessed that he struggled on these trips; that they represented an uneasy choice between honouring lifelong friendships and being true to the values and opinions you'd formed as a maturing individual. I found myself agreeing, and started to think about Kelly. She'd like Krakow with its Old Town, salt mines, castle and central square.

When we returned from the scene of more than a million deaths for the final evening of 'Steak 'n' Tits' followed by the 'Tottie Tour', our mood was understandably sombre and we were unable to share in the gang's enthusiasm for more naked flesh. This caused a bit of an argument, opening up fissures in this disparate group that had politely held together so far, largely thanks to massive levels of inebriation. Myself and Chris were castigated for spoiling the party vibe and ignoring the protests of the party during the breakfast debate over what to do with the day. The others had gone paint-balling. For the sake of harmony and Rick's last night of partying, we tagged along for a final round of strip clubs.

**12.00 p.m.** Checked my account balance. Rick was right about the cost, thanks to the strength of Sterling it was no more expensive than a big weekend in London.

### Sunday 27 June, 2004

**3.45 p.m. Home.** Our kitchen has had a makeover – rebranded with the blue and white stripes of the Tesco Value range. With next month's ill-timed holiday to consider, we waddled around the supermarket like a pair of penny-pinching pensioners, clutching our shopping list and calculator to ensure we didn't overshoot our meagre budget. The baked beans I had for lunch afterwards were revolting – like chewing on sugar-coated pellets.

### Tuesday 13 July 2004

**6.39 p.m. The Counting House.** Returned from our adventures and the blazing heat of the Croatian sun to the cooler winds of home. Weary from travel, we had a fractious exchange at the ATM after landing, when neither of us could withdraw any money to pay for the extortionately priced airport connection. Exasperated by our farcical predicament and the less than appealing prospect of standing on the hard shoulder to hitch a lift with a psychopathic lorry driver, I began shouting at Kelly, laying into her for never taking any responsibility and always assuming I had things covered. Felt bad about my outburst as she rummaged in her bag with tears rolling down her face, eventually producing her cheque book. My guilt intensified on the train, when I realised that she'd effectively paid double fare, what with the impending bank charge she'd incur for her rubber cheque.

The trip was pure folly though – not for the first time, all credit has expired and I'm back on Poor Street. A week ago, I was living like a Roman Emperor on the Dalmatian Coast, and now I'm counting loose change into plastic bank bags to buy the shopping.

### Wednesday 14 July, 2004
**9.55 a.m. Office.** Gulp! Logged on to my accounts to assess the damage – situation critical – both cards up to the limit. Way to go dickhead. That's me well and truly in it up to my sunburnt neck. Feel a bit dizzy, must be a bout of financial vertigo.

**10.15 a.m.** From now on there's going to be a new order, I'll be living on what's left of my salary and won't be using any cards. The fact that they're maxed out is beside the point.

**1.15 p.m.** Three hours of serious industry. First, tidied my desk, then called and emailed everyone who's been chasing me, as if a flurry of diligence and productivity would somehow bring order to my life and help quash the feeling that it's all about to come crashing down. Unfortunately, my debts are still here and I'm still in the shit. Deep, deep shit.

### Thursday 15 July, 2004
**10.30 a.m. Office.** Payday today. Opened wage slip in the vain hope of a miraculously improved situation. Am waking up to the fact that the party's over. It's remarkable how quickly it's come grinding to a halt. The fantasy kingdom in which I've been lording it up these past couple of years has evaporated and I'm about to confront a bleak reality.

**11.45 a.m.** Did a few quick calculations and got depressed at the sight of the balance sheet. It'll be a real test trying to live on what's left. Been staring at my sums for the last hour racking my brains to try and find some room for manoeuvre. First things first: look at restructuring and see where it leaves me. Time for pragmatism. Chin up.

### Monday 19 July, 2004

**12.45 p.m. Work.** My downfall has been confirmed by the introduction of the plastic lunchbox. Attempting to be positive, Kelly suggested I go 'back to skool' and get myself a 'Masters of the Universe' design as it would look kitschy. But it's hard to keep the humour when even a Wagon Wheel is an extravagance. Bumped into Bruce Clacton, the only other nerd eating out of a lunchbox, at the fridge earlier, while collecting my tuck. As he moved aside to let me through, he mumbled something about there being 'no such thing as a free lunch.' Somebody save me please.

### Tuesday 20 July, 2004

**11.15 a.m. Office.** A breakthrough. In a fit of inspiration, I telephoned the bank this morning, having scrutinised the details of my graduate loan. Turns out I've been paying almost a hundred quid a month on *Payment Protection Insurance* – a pointless product if ever there was one. The drone on the phone confirmed that 'PPI' is optional, so I'm counting the minutes till lunchtime.

**1.00 p.m.** The new branch of HSBC on Mare Street is one of those ultra-modern, open-plan affairs with minimal staff, lots of automated machines and no cashiers, which is one way of avoiding a hold-up. Found myself locked in one of the fishbowl cubicles, sitting across from a woman in her forties, who listened to my request and my need to free up some money, before doing her utmost to try and discourage me.

'I understand that you want to reduce your monthly payments, Mr Livingson, but with the size of your loan, this probably isn't a wise course of action. If your debt was only a couple of thousand, I wouldn't normally bat an eyelid but this is a considerable loan, and I must make you aware that the bank would expect it to continue to be repaid, should you encounter financial difficulty.'

For a brief moment I almost bought into it, before remembering the figures on my desk.

'But I'm in a secure job,' I said curtly.

She persisted. Clasping her hands for effect, leaning forward across the desk, and in a worried voice, she said: 'Well you might be alright now, but you never know what's round the corner.'

The only thing missing was the music from *Jaws*, when the shark begins circling the boat. This woman was brilliantly trained to make me feel desperate and anxious, but I held firm. Unflinching, I insisted that she prepare the requisite paperwork so I could be on my way.

### Tuesday 27 July, 2004
**1.55 p.m. Office.** Lunch was a particularly cheerless affair today. It'd been a desultory morning and I'd exhausted myself doing nothing. Each time I decided to try and work, out of desperation or for something to stop time from dragging, I would immediately give up when it became clear I might have to make a telephone call or actually leave my seat.

I headed out on the stroke of midday, consumed with lethargy and even unable to get excited by the imminent selection of my food, which I usually looked upon as a highlight of the working day. As I waited for my cheese and bean jacket potato in the workers' café, amongst bantering builders and sad solitary pensioners, I realised that I came here every Tuesday, and that almost without exception I ate a potato of some description. It then occurred to me that I was wearing one of my pastel shirts, also part of a pattern, making them more colourful as the week progressed. Come Friday, I would be wearing a fashion shirt to reflect a more upbeat mood and signal the arrival of the weekend. I began to feel terribly depressed as I realised that everything in my life followed an established order. Monday was supermarket night, Wednesday was football after work, Thursday often involved drinks or some form of social engagement and so on.

I looked at the clock. In less than half an hour, I would be back in the office. The novelty of that situation had certainly worn off. The faces in there had become familiar. They were just ordinary people you found anywhere else. The same concerns, obsessions and habits. The same likes and dislikes. Less exciting. More like they were and less like they seemed. Just people.

Everything had become depressingly ordinary. The streets were no longer sprinkled with magic dust – they were just cold grey slabs of concrete that led from one place to another. I had lost my immunity and was now a real citizen with real problems like everyone else. The supply of money had dried up and with it, my ability to purchase new distractions. There would be no more novelty to mask the reality of every new day. I had exhausted all possibilities.

Having mechanically ingested my forgettable food, I sipped at my tea and stared out of the window. I really didn't want to go back to the office. I thought about saying that I was unwell and needed to go home. The impending boredom and constraint were too terrifying to contemplate and I actually began to feel nauseous. But it felt like too much trouble even to put on the illness. So I paid up and robotically began the walk back to work, feeling heavy and deadened.

As I walked back into the stuffy room, people were busy getting on with things. How did they do it? How did they motivate themselves? I sat down and re-opened my document and felt my heart breaking. An old memory came to me. It was a summer's day like this one. A group of us had cut out of school and driven to a nearby river. I could see us all in our underwear standing on the arched wall of the stone bridge, our skinny teenage frames rowdy and boisterous as we goaded one another, legs wobbling with nerves before we eventually found the courage to jump...

### Thursday 29 July, 2004
**4.30 p.m. Office.** Today's big headline news is the announcement from the Bank of England that UK consumer debt has broken through the £1 trillion mark for the first time.

According to the appropriately named Charles Bean, the Bank of England's chief economist, despite the record debt mountain, we are *not* sitting on a 'time-bomb'. I'd like to invite Mr Bean to come and take a peek under my chair, as it seems to be making a rather worrying ticking sound.

I can't help but compare Mr Bean's questionable assurances to those of Tariq Aziz as he stood on the banks of the Euphrates trying to convince the world that Iraq was on the brink of victory while Baghdad exploded behind him. I'm no economist but surely a trillion pounds isn't sustainable. That kind of accountancy doesn't add up.

# The Proletariat Playboys

*'Natwest, Natwest – Barclays – Midlands – Lloyds*
*Black horse apocalypse*
*Death sanitised through credit.'*

Manic Street Preachers,
Natwest, Natwest – Barclays – Midlands – Lloyds

**Wednesday 4 August, 2004**

**8.37 p.m. Home.** It's Rick. He's finally sent through details of his wedding plans in September, which only happens to be in bloody *Sicily* of all places. I've also been bestowed with the honour of best man duties, so non-attendance is out of the question. When I broke the news to Kelly, I thought she was going to hit me. She's adamant I tell Rick we can't afford it and is refusing to discuss it further. The Croatia trip nearly finished us off, another holiday now would be pure insanity.

Saw this on the web: *'The list of "celebs" who over the years have honored Taormina with their presence is long. To name but a few: Austria's Empress Elisabeth "Sissi", the British kings Edward VII and George V, Greta Garbo, Marlene Dietrich, Joan Crawford, Rita Hayworth, Cary Grant, Sofia Loren, Elisabeth Taylor, Richard Burton and Christian Dior.'*

Problem solved. All I need do is regale Kelly with the list of celebrities whose footsteps we'll be following in and she'll be unable to contain her excitement.

Also checked the hotels and flights – she's right, there's simply no way we can find that sort of money, not even for a trans-Europe Mega-Bus.

**9.30 p.m.** Of course there is one way in which I could fulfil my ceremonial duties – by returning the Mint credit card offer that arrived last week. Yet another new brand has been launched onto the market, and Rick's RSVP isn't the only invitation I've received recently. They've really been pushing this one, with billboards and TV adverts loudly proclaiming the virtues of the 'MC2' and its unique design: it has a *curved* bottom-right corner – a radical departure from the boring cards of the past with their four straight edges.

Obviously, the marketing men at Mint have obeyed the fundamental principles of consumerism – to constantly update old models and produce new designs in order to stimulate perpetual consumption. But I don't care for their gimmicks, I just want their money. When I think about it, another few hundred will hardly make a difference to the grand total.

**11.30 p.m.** From the counting house to the doghouse: huge ding-dong with Kelly – our first real bust-up – sparked by me revealing my Mint Card plan. As she rapped on the table, pointed and yelled, everything she said made sense; it was demented even to be considering it. But the 'discussion' only made me furious with frustration, since I was in the utterly maddening position of arguing for something I didn't even agree with.

In spite of this, my irrational refusal to accept her point only enraged her further, and she brought the debate to an abrupt close, telling me, 'Go by yourself. I'm not having any part in it'. Arrgh! We both agree that it's madness. But I can't let him down. I've been friends with Rick since we were crapping into newspaper and setting it alight on people's doorsteps.

**Wednesday 18 August, 2004**
**12.00 p.m. Work.** I'm half tempted to confess all. To come clean and announce to the world that I've screwed up, just to relieve myself of the burden. But I can just imagine the insufferable reaction if I did: the initial disbelief, the incredulity, the reproach, the disparaging comments, and finally, after all the commotion, the tedious moralising.

*HOW MUCH?*
*But you must've known what you were doing?*
*Only an idiot would get themselves in such a mess.*
*Why did you carry on?*
*Why on earth didn't you stop borrowing and sort yourself out?*
*Well, paying it back will teach you the value of money.*

No, it's all too easy to predict, and I don't think I could stomach playing the lead in 'The Fool and His Folly Exposed'. It's one of life's rules: none of us want to be seen as stupid so we keep quiet and carry on.

### Friday 20 August, 2004

**10.15 a.m. Office.** I used to really look forward to payday. Now it's just a regular reminder of how done-for I am. I'm left with nowt but loose change and a month's worth of plastic lunchboxes at my desk. Work without reward, a truly miserable situation.

**10.45 a.m.** I've really screwed myself over. I can only see one way out of this situation and that's to try and earn my way out of it. Which means looking around for a better job. But for more money, any prospective employer's going to want their pound of flesh – sixty hours a week *and* your soul.

It's been a long time since this wide-eyed whippersnapper nursed his dream of making it into the boardroom. I've already had enough of this working life, I've seriously had enough. Meetings make me suicidal, careerists are contemptible morons. When I put on these hideous clothes, I feel incredibly uncomfortable, completely inauthentic. To survive in this world you have to be able to play the game, but it's a schizophrenic charade that shatters my being.

**11.00 p.m. Home.** Arrived home this evening with an irrepressible urge to try and express my feelings. For the first time in months, I sat myself down and began writing; a kind of loose and wandering stream of consciousness. Incoherent ramblings no doubt, but nobody is going to see it. It's funny how strange life seems when you actually start thinking about it and try to describe it. Kelly arrived home to find me at the kitchen table.

'What are you doing, are you writing?' she asked tentatively, poking her head around the door.

'Yeah, no, not really,' I said shiftily, feeling a little embarrassed.

'That's cool. Don't clam up. I'll leave you alone.' The interruption wasn't altogether untimely, I was on my third glass of wine and feeling a little woozy.

'It's alright, I was just messing about.'

'What are you writing about?'

'Acting,' I blurted out.

'You want to be an actor?'

'No – I am an actor. I feel like an actor every day,' I explained cagily. 'I was thinking about how much of our lives we spend pretending. Every day we go to work, the whole time we're playing at being someone else, we project this kind of perverted representation of ourselves that isn't the real us. We're not being true to ourselves and yet everybody does it.'

'That's heavy stuff,' said Kelly sounding intrigued. 'I think I know what you mean though…'

'I was looking round the office today, thinking about people's behaviour and what they're like outside their jobs. It struck me as very unnatural, scary almost, how everybody wears two faces and how easily they switch between the two. It's like you've got a public face and your true face. It's proper schizo stuff when you think about it.'

'I suppose it is…' she said pensively, 'when you put it like that.'

'To me that's what professionalism is – pretending,' I said, feeling slightly light-headed. 'When somebody tells you that you should be more *professional*, what they really mean is that you need to be less real. It's like they're saying, you can't be too real in here.'

'I hate that,' said Kelly.

'But it's totally fucked up, this acceptance that we have to be two different people. People shouldn't have to put on a mask, they should be their real selves all of the time. Don't you think?'

'I like this,' she said nodding, 'it's interesting. It's good that you're trying to write about it.'

'Sometimes,' I continued, 'I get these moments, when I suddenly get this horrible heightened awareness of myself – usually when I hear myself talking to someone or catch sight of myself in the window of the meeting room. It doesn't feel like it's me; it feels like it's somebody playing me on a stage… And then I realise that *it is me* and it creeps me out. That's how I know it's wrong. I don't know, it's hard to explain. Maybe I'm going mad.'

'I wouldn't worry about it,' she said smiling.

'I mean when you take a step back and start analysing the way we conduct our lives, all the bizarre daily rituals and what we take to be acceptable behaviour… That's when I start to believe there's no such thing as sanity – that the whole world is demented and populated by madmen.'

'I'm not sure if that makes me feel better or worse,' said Kelly dryly.

I got up and pulled the plug on a new bottle of wine, extracting the cork with a low plunk. We moved into the lounge with our glasses and sat there in silence, without the distraction of the TV or the stereo. It was late evening by this point. The sun had disappeared behind the houses on the other side of the street and we sat near one another in semi-darkness, like two figures in an old painting. Kelly was in the chair with her back to the window and I struggled to make out her facial expression against the half-light. My thoughts had switched slightly and I began to reminisce.

I began thinking about when I'd lived wildly, when I'd bounced from one binge to the next with no restrictions. When I thought about that time, I realised *that* was when I had felt most alive. I was alive now too, but only in the sense that I existed. Sure I was younger then, but everything was tinged with excitement, you believed anything was possible.

'There was something authentic to my life when I was younger,' I said. 'I was at least true to myself. That's the feeling I want to get back again. I want to be authentic, I'm not totally sure what I mean, but it sounds right.'

'Without the same drug binges,' Kelly said.

'Without resorting to drugs,' I said agreeing with a laugh.

'So what do you do?' asked Kelly raising her glass to her lips, her chair shrouded in the orange glow of the street lamp. I had no immediate reply and we both remained silent for some time. Then Kelly got up and I stretched out on the sofa, happy to think my own thoughts, basking in my red grape reverie.

### Monday 23 August, 2004

Application pending. My new card's taking an age to arrive and the wedding's in four weeks. Wouldn't be too upset if they were to decline me – at least it'd provide me with a genuine get-out.

**Sunday 29 August, 2004**

**11.30 a.m. Home**. Out for Big Dave's birthday last night. Turned out one of his boys, Sparky, had hired a limo to drive us around the city for a few hours before heading on to Spearmint Rhino. Felt like a right tube with half the street gawping at us as we all climbed into the big black Hummer (complete with tinted windows) that pulled up outside the pub.

When the driver welcomed us aboard 'the party bus', he wasn't exaggerating. It was a mobile nightclub on wheels, fully kitted out with a bar, cinema system and a mirrored ceiling which ran the length of the cabin. Sparky took control of the DVD player and played hardcore porn for the duration. One of the lads kept turning it up to full volume and winding the windows down, drawing confused looks from crowds of revellers on the pavement. It's amazing how many people strain to catch a glimpse of who's in a limo, no doubt expecting to see the likes of Tom Cruise. The whole experience is intended to make you feel important or like a celebrity. I just felt like a prize twat.

Our tour took in all the major sights and we drove around the city for three hours with twenty blokes wedged together guzzling champagne and sniffing coke to a kaleidoscope of various orifices, penetrations and ejaculations. Ours wasn't the only *Party Bus* on the roads; I'd never really noticed before, but central London on a Saturday night is crawling with the things. I even clocked a bright pink clunker carrying a load of hens that nearly took out a rickshaw driver on Charing Cross Road. When I relayed the evening to Kelly, she said it was possibly the most crass thing she'd ever heard. Only redeemed myself when I told her how I'd quietly snuck off home during the confusion of everybody trying to get in to a strip joint.

**Tuesday 31 August, 2004**

**1.30 p.m. Office.** *Get Mint, Get More* (indebted). Card arrived this morning. Booked hotel and flights at a premium due to 11th hour booking. '*This is pure lunacy,*' I thought to myself as I collected yet another batch of reservations from the office printer. Well, at least we'll be there in the photos wearing a veneer of affluence, our strained smiles masking a precarious reality.

**1.45 p.m.** Feel sick thinking about what I've just done. I can't even look forward to the trip, what with all the trouble it's caused and knowing there'll be another bill to juggle on my return.

**Wednesday 15 September, 2004**

**10.15 a.m. Office.** My income-to-outgoings ratio has passed a tipping point. Real money runs out in a matter of days and I'm forced to be overdrawn just to get through the month. As a result, the bank is hammering me with penalty charges, which only compound the problem. What really gets me is the way they let you foul up so they can sting you afterwards. It's all set up to cream profits.

**10.30 a.m.** HSBC – the world's local bank my arse. Telephoned the bank to complain, and got through to Bombay. Should've hung up immediately instead of wasting my breath appealing in vain to someone on the other side of the world with absolutely zero decision-making power. Regardless, I still found myself trying to reason with the guy, 'How can you expect me to sort my account out if you keep whacking on charges every month?' I pleaded. Eventually terminated the call when I found myself unsuccessfully trying to explain the principle of Catch-22. They're reviewing my complaint and will respond in writing.

**Friday 17 September, 2004**
**6.00 p.m. Home.** Letter from the bank. A standard template explaining their charging structure and a copy of the terms and conditions. Nothing like a sympathetic ear in times of trouble. My misfortune = their profit. Quite different from the way they portray themselves in the adverts.

**11.00 p.m.** It's the big wedding in Sicily this weekend. On our return we plan to sit down and see what we can do to sort ourselves out.

**Wednesday 22 September, 2004**
**7.00 p.m. Home.** Well that's another card up to its limit. Can't deny we didn't have a great time – when you've made your decision you might as well enjoy the experience. But the fun was tempered by the guilt of spending more borrowed money and the irrepressible feeling of edging ever closer to implosion. I'd like to say the happy couple appreciated it, but I don't think anybody was aware just how much of a strain it was for us to attend.

**Friday 24 September, 2004**
**11.00 a.m. Office.** Hang my head – I am now skanking farewell cards. One of the employees, Anne, is leaving. When the card reached my desk, I scribbled a suitably banal 'good luck and all the best', took a furtive peek around to see if anyone was looking, and dumped it back in the envelope *sans* contribution. Felt like a real tightwad but the tax-dodging contractor in question has only been here five months, and she's ratting off to another assignment on double my wages.

**3.45 p.m.** The ceremonial huddle around Anne's desk has just broken. The customary goodbye speech was marked by a few tears from Anne, although the trauma of parting was softened by the presentation of a £75 House of Fraser voucher, which she gaily announced will buy her a new pair of shoes. Vindication for my frugality – I'm in no position to be subsidising a supermodel's wardrobe.

### Saturday 25 September, 2004
**5.30 p.m. Home.** Rick's emailed some of the wedding photos. Although they were unable to broker a suitable deal with *OK Magazine* they needn't be disappointed – they've captured the time. There we are, myself and Kelly in the big group shot, lined up with everybody, beaming away as if we hadn't a care in the world.

It sure looks special: everybody on the terrace in the sunshine, with the bay shimmering in the distance. The perfect scene. Nobody looking at the picture would see the invisible clouds of debt hanging over us. And that's just it; the vast amounts of debt that people are quietly racking up, nobody talks about it, but it's there in the background, looming ever larger. Still we smile for the camera, both of us wearing our masks, maintaining a stupid bloody pretence that everything's chipper instead of calling time on this madness. Denial and pretence – a lethal combination and a pitiful sham. And for what exactly? To get about like a bunch of C-list celebrities with our vulgar attempts at mimicking their lifestyles. Weekends in Europe, weddings on exotic islands or a rock star limo into town, once the preserve of the rich and famous, now available to all. The bar of expectation has been raised and anyone can be king for a day – or upto the limit on their card.

# Reality Cheque

*'Debt is the slavery of the free.'*

Publilius Syrus, Roman author, 1st century BC

**Sunday 26 September, 2004**
**8.00 p.m.** Myself and Kelly have drawn up a plan to get out of debt which is now pinned to the fridge door:
*1. NO to all stag, hen and wedding parties abroad.*
*2. Restructure and consolidate all debt.*
*3. Earn more money.*

**Thursday 30 September, 2004**
**10.45 a.m. Office.** Letter from EGG advising me to convert my credit card balance into a personal loan (with themselves of course) and benefit from a lower interest rate. Made the call and the agreement is on its way to me.

**Friday 8 October, 2004**
**6.45 p.m. Doormat.** Confirmation of new loan arrangement with EGG. Had to structure it over the longest terms available to keep outgoings to a minimum. A few years living above your means equals a lifetime of debt. In this case, 84 monthly repayments continuing into the next decade. Makes Christ's 40 days in the desert look like a holiday.

**Friday 15 October, 2004**
**7.30 p.m. Home.** Playing Scrabble tonight over a few tins with Kelly. We've been living the high life ever since we got together, and this hardship's new territory for us. She put things nicely into context: 'I don't know how I did it before I met you, but I always managed it. It was a struggle but I got through. I'd have egg on toast for dinner and drink Tesco's lager. We don't need expensive food and fancy holidays'. Thanks to our benevolent Mayor, we're off to the National History Museum tomorrow, as it's a free day out.

### Saturday 30 October, 2004

**6.15 p.m. Home.** Think I may have found the answer to the emptiness of the work-spend merry-go-round – my weekends are now dedicated to serious reading. As soon as Kelly heads out to practice on Saturday morning, I have the place to myself and all the headspace a man could want. At first she was suspicious of my behaviour, suspecting me of having another woman on the go. It wasn't until she witnessed it for herself that she knew I was for real.

'Are you taking notes?' she said, surprised to find me still at my desk.

'Uh-huh, I like copying out my favourite passages or important bits where something's being said.'

'That's very studious, Mr Professor,' she said, lurching forward to wrap me in a bear hug. She always returned home in playful mood after a day's singing.

We raided the cupboards and managed to put together a good meal of lamb and wine, which for once felt like a deserved reward rather than a tired bourgeois pleasure. Well alright, it was still pretty bourgeois.

### Tuesday 9 November, 2004

**2.30 p.m. Office.** One loan or two? Called HSBC to arrange consolidation of Gold Card into Graduate Loan. All too familiar drill: need to pop in and agree the paperwork.

### Thursday 11 November, 2004

**2.05 p.m. Office.** Back from the bank, where my new best mate, the jovial little chirpster 'Daz' Chatterton, cheerfully assisted me in my demise. I explained that this was to be my final consolidation exercise, sounding rather like an alcoholic marking his last drink. Darren assured me I was 'doing the sensible thing', and let me know his door was always open – 'if you've any problems at all then come and see me'. I feigned an urgent meeting to escape his faux friendliness and left as quickly as possible.

**2.15 p.m.** It's hammering it down now, the rain's making such a noise that people have left their desks to press their faces to the window and watch it bouncing off the pavement. All the lights are on in the office. It's so dark outside, it feels like the middle of the night. Graduate Loan is now over £200 a month until my release date in 2012. 2012, sounds like the title of a sci-fi novel. I wish it *were* fiction: a story about somebody else I could put down and walk away from. But I can't. It's real and it's my life, or what's left of it. I'll be nearly 40 by the time I'm free.

**2.30 p.m.** It's still lashing it down outside. A scraggy middle-aged guy from facilities management is strategically placing buckets across the floor to catch the drips from the leaking roof. Hope it caves in.

**2.35 p.m.** Incredibly this is the first time I've ever read a copy of one of my loan agreements. That sentence at the bottom of the page that says: *95 further monthly repayments, on the same day in each month thereafter*. I'm basically enslaved to the banks for the next decade. I have signed my life away. There's nothing more I can do now.

**2.40 p.m.** Calculated that by the time it's paid off, I'll have paid the bank a third of the loan amount again just in interest charges. Over two years dedicated to the payment of interest, working solely for the bank's gain, and that's just on this loan.

Might as well turn up for work wearing the uniform of a bank clerk. Aarrrgh. Need to stop this, just too painful. Sending myself round the twist.

**3.00 p.m.** Drawn up yet another budget plan now that my final consolidation exercise is complete. Things are marginally better, but the minimum payments are still massive. Depressed.

**4.00 p.m.** Decided on an early departure today, haven't the temperament to be in the company of other people. I'd rather sit and brood in the privacy of my own quarters.

**4.30 p.m. Home**. Plan to plough through a six-pack and drown my sorrows.

**5.45 p.m.** It hasn't stopped chucking it down all day. The trees in the street are taking a real battering, leaves swirling in the storm. From my window I can see people returning to their houses in the evening gloom, struggling against the wind and rain.

### Friday 12 November, 2004
**9.30 p.m. Home.** I'm trying to keep my spirits up, but it's impossible to prevent the Black Dog from visiting. Kelly's trying her best to console me, but there's no escaping that I've ruined my life.

### Monday 15 November, 2004
**10.45 a.m. Work.** Bah, payday and the full effect of my consolidation loans is felt. A few quick sums confirm what I already know – that I'm just working to exist. What kind of a life is that?

# Arbeit Macht Frei

*'Personal debt has grown twice as fast as income since 1997 when New Labour took office. On average, personal debt has increased by 50%, while incomes have risen by 23%.'*

Credit Action, 2004

## Saturday 1 January, 2005

**4.30 p.m. Home.** Took a call from the boys in Australia on Christmas day, they'd been barbecuing on the beach. They kept asking when we were coming out to see them. Unfortunately, 'I can't afford it' looks like it's going to be my mantra for 2005. Determined to use this year to clear some debt. I want to be free again. As things stand, my life's on pause, destined to stagnate until it's all paid off.

## Friday 7 January, 2005

**3.00 p.m. Office.** Things have moved quickly. Reluctantly spent the week on the phone to an employment agency in the city. You could be forgiven for thinking you'd called a sex hotline, the female consultants are so flirty they're practically blowing you down the phone as they work it for their commission. I remember Justin telling me he once jacked off when one of them called him at home – he said her voice was so sexy he couldn't resist. Covert wanking aside, the upshot of all this phone-flirting is that I'm starting a new job in four weeks.

**6.30 p.m. Home.** A journey of a thousand repayments begins with a single timesheet. Based on my new hourly rate, I'm looking at a regime of 45 hours a week for at least the next three years. Any slippage and it'll quickly become four, five or six of my best years lost to serious hard work. Really don't think I've got the stomach for it. But have to at least try.

**8.00 p.m.** I can see it all panning out: I'll get myself out of this mess right around the time Kelly's biological clock starts sounding its alarm. My chance of doing anything with my life will be gone. Life sets you traps, you fall in and before you know it, you're bitter, old and twisted. Black Dog's back. Time for a very big drink.

### Saturday 20 February, 2005

**10.30 a.m. Home.** Yesterday's farewell ritual was a rather subdued affair, lacking the usual celebratory excitement brought on by the success of promotion or new beginnings. When the clock signalled it was time for the office to descend on my desk and encircle me in that unnerving cluster for the final moment, with all those faces staring at me in expectation of a witty anecdote of my time here, I just felt numb. My usual wit was too far buried in my melancholy soul, so I hurriedly mumbled a standard line or two about how much I'd enjoyed it here and how I'd miss everyone, desperate to get it over with. In spite of my reluctance, I agreed to a few drinks in the pub afterwards. Thankfully, my colleagues were charitable enough, and made sure I didn't have to buy a round all night. I have no recollection of how it all ended.

### Monday 21 February, 2005

**9.00 a.m. Office.** Day one on the road to repayment. Up before daybreak for a long commute across the city to Brixton. The slog starts here. It's the only way out. God I'm poor.

**11.00 a.m.** This place is a grisly tomb. Got a bad feeling about it already. Walked in this morning and it reeked of death, nobody talking, just the tap-tap-tapping of keyboards.

### Wednesday 23 February, 2005

**1.24 p.m. Office.** Praying for payday. Currently dining on a diet of synthetic supermarket sandwiches washed down with tap water. Earlier, I extracted a rogue pubic hair from my mayonnaise sodden triangle, and hurled the remainder at the bin outside the office in disgust. Only I missed, and the bread hit the wall where it stuck fast, remaining like a rotting contribution to street art.

### Sunday 27 February, 2005

**1.30 p.m. Home.** Caught up with Big Dave last night. He was looking tanned and relaxed. Well, he's just returned from a five-week trip to Australia visiting the boys, and he's off to Africa on safari in a few weeks. As I listened to his tales of travel and adventure, it struck me that our meeting had the air of a cured drunk encountering one of his old bar buddies who's still living the life. Back to rehab for me tomorrow.

### Wednesday 2 March, 2005

**9.45 a.m. Work.** Have been desperately hoping that my misgivings about this place might prove wrong, but I'm afraid there's more life in a cemetery. To my great misfortune, I've been planted between two first class tweakers without an ounce of zip between them.

Opposite me sits Sean Mullen, who barely manages a 'good morning' and remains fairly mute for the rest of the day. At first I thought he was just shy, but I've come to realise that his sustained silence is actually the product of a perceived superiority. I suspect arrogance because of the way he carries himself, swanning about dressed like a city lawyer: full suit and tie, shiny cufflinks, immaculately polished shoes and an ultra-dynamic slicked-back hair-do. He turns up every morning swinging a suspiciously lightweight leather attaché case and clutching his second favourite prop: a giant bucket of Starbucks coffee. Instead of throwing them away, he leaves the empty cartons to accumulate on his desk for show.

Despite hailing from the land of sunshine, Mullen is the antithesis of the stereotypical Australian – he's so pale that more than ten minutes in the sun would probably kill him. Tall, thin and rickety, on the rare occasions when he ventures out from behind his desk, he creaks around the office like a lost corpse searching for the graveyard.

Hemming me in on the other side is Chris Fell – a different model from the same factory. Like Mullen, he's been programmed with an inhuman capacity for remaining in stiff silence, as he pores over the contents of his phenomenally dull documents. Although barely 30, he has the demeanour of a middle-aged man, and mopes around the office wearing a perpetual frown. To stroll in on the brightest of mornings and be confronted by the sight of his dour expression can be utterly deflating.

Short and frumpy, dowdy little Fell plods around the place in a wardrobe consisting of items sourced exclusively from the *Council Clothing Catalogue*. You can hear the squeak of his rubber-soled boat shoes and the flapping of his baggy turn-ups swishing from side-to-side as he walks along the corridor. It's impossible to look at Fell and not find him offensive. His pallid face has been made jowly from a daily diet of office treats. To watch him returning to his desk clutching another sugary reward for his hours of application is to witness the tragic high point of a small man's day.

But despite his farcical appearance and distasteful manner, Fell's one to be wary of. A genuine man of the establishment, he's actively targeting the vacant 'Deputy Team Leader' position. Apparently he instigated the sacking of my predecessor for too many coffee breaks and for fiddling his timesheet. I can feel his sullen stare upon me as I work, and he always seems to make his presence felt whenever I decide it's time for a quick surf.

Christ, it's enough that I should serve my sentence, but someone's played a sick joke lumping me in with these two.

**2.45 p.m. Office.** I have definitely landed in purgatory. Popped downstairs for a meeting and clocked former colleague, peroxide princess Anne, sitting at one of the stations.

**Saturday 5 March, 2005**
**11.45 a.m. Home.** It's not quite the Gulag, but this new regime is definitely a ball-breaker. I'm up at 6.30 every morning feeling bleary-eyed and utterly flailed. But these early starts and long days are already taking their toll – come Friday I'm aching with tiredness and home seems very far away.

I'd been thinking about my bed all afternoon yesterday, and dove straight into it the moment I stepped in. Kelly was already home and feeling frisky, misinterpreting my dash for the duvet to climb in with me. I moaned and groaned in irritation as she tried to instigate some early evening fun.

I eventually woke from my nap, desperate for a cold beer and tranquillity, to a woman affronted and untimely accusations of a relationship in decline: 'It's all downhill from here… I remember the days when you couldn't keep your hands off me and I'd be fighting you off'. Her words made me feel about as potent as a pensioner and it wasn't until I'd drained the first beer bottle that I regained the ability to speak and perked up a little. But the tank was still empty; my reserves were drained and in need of real replenishment. I must have hit a wall round about 11 and woke up on the sofa fully dressed. No wonder high-fliers in punishing jobs turn to stimulants.

Thank god Saturday has arrived. My only exertion will be to skim off some of my first pay cheque and pick up a basket of good stuff for dinner. The smell of sizzling steak and the luxury of the grape – there must be some reward, something to justify the great sacrifice of your days.

**Wednesday 9 March, 2005**
**2.25 p.m. Office.** Brixton has just elevated itself. Headed down Coldharbour Lane to treat myself to something decent for lunch and happened upon on a sanctuary for my soul, a magical literary grotto called 'Book Mongers'. As I stepped in and began poking around, feverishly scanning the stacked shelves of second-hand tomes, all smartly arranged, I felt that nervous rushing buzz I used to get in libraries as a boy. It hit all the right notes: bookcases spilling over into stacked piles on the floor, rare and quirky collectibles exhibited behind the counter, and the affable proprietor who chatted easily and knowledgably with a regular customer. They even had a battered couch on the raised area at the back of the store to encourage lengthy perusing, which I took advantage of, having found a biography of Albert Camus to devour.

Back in the uninspiring confines of the office, twenty minutes late and offering no explanation or apology, I pulled out my notebook and chuckled at the quote I'd copied out: 'Which is the more aesthetic form of suicide, forty hours a week or a shotgun?' This caused the sour-faced Fell to impertinently ask me what I found so funny? *Your fucking face,* I thought as I flat-batted him with my dismissal, turning to stare out of the window and fantasising about one day running my own place, dreaming of hosting readings in a candle-lit basement on wild drunken nights.

**Sunday 12 March, 2005**

**8.30 p.m. Home.** The old man left his prejudice at home and came down to London for a day's sightseeing, including a ride on the London Eye. Kelly and I met him and Jan on the Southbank for a drink. Don't know what possessed me, but I told him I'd bid farewell to job security to tackle my debts. It was his chance to say 'I told you so'.

'I warned you, didn't I. I told you about those bloody things but y'wouldn't listen. You 'ave to go your own sweet way. Your mother was the same, always wanting what we couldn't afford. Cleaned me out she did.'

Jan gave him a look, they'd had a nice day, she didn't want him spoiling it with his preaching.

'How much do you owe then?' he snapped.

'I'm not telling you,' I said, clamming up. He'd be horrified, and I'd never hear the end of it if he knew how reckless I'd been.

'Well, it must be a lot if you won't even tell me.'

The waitress arrived with our dinners: four beef and ale pies. He didn't persist with the line of enquiry as we waited for our food to cool, opting for more condemnation.

'Well you're paying the price for it. You'll never have a safer job than local government, and what about your pension eh?' he said, ignoring Jan's frowns.

I shrugged my shoulders. 'I got a bit carried away alright. I'm on the case. This job's much better paid. Let's just leave it at that, shall we?' I didn't have the strength for a confrontation in my current frame of mind, but he was like a dog with its favourite bone.

'Maybe this'll teach you the value of money. It only takes a second to spend it, but hours to earn.'

Jan could see I wasn't in the mood and made a bid to change the subject. 'C'mon, enough of the lecture, tell him our news,' she interjected, coming to my aid.

'Aye, I've been meaning to tell you for a while,' he started.

'You've finally agreed to a vasectomy,' I quipped, suddenly finding my funny bone.

'Watch y'tongue y'cheeky bastard,' he said, turning a little red. Jan and Kelly were both suppressing giggles.

'If y'must know, we've been sitting on a bit of land. An orchard at the back of some houses on the Riverside Estate. We're building ourselves a house on it. I've always wanted to do it and now the bank's given us the green light. We started work about a month ago.'

I summoned as much interest as I could to avoid returning to my situation, prompting him to pull out the builder's plans he'd conveniently brought with him in his rucksack. The four of us sat around the table in the pub as he talked us through every stage of the Grand Project. We made for home as soon as it was polite to do so, and sat on the bus battling with the aftermath of the stodgy gravy pie that was busily repeating on us.

**Friday 1 April, 2005**
**10.00 a.m. Office.** Starting to see the money roll in. Began the process of repayment by knocking a few hundred off the Mint card.

**11.15 a.m.** Fear that I've just triggered an existential crisis. Decided I'd keep a track of things, so spent the last two hours constructing the *spreadsheet of death*: an Excel document mapping out the next few years in terms of paydays and payments. Faced with such a bleak future, I should do the sensible thing by getting up and walking out. Failing that, just end it all.

**12.45 p.m.** Reopened spreadsheet after lunch to see if I couldn't find some way of reducing its span. Nothing doing unless I can convince Kelly of the benefits of squatting.

**11.45 p.m. Home.** Unsurprisingly, I made for poor company tonight, managing to deflate Kelly's buoyant Friday feeling by first refusing to go out for dinner and then sounding like my dad by complaining about unnecessary cost. I subsequently proceeded to grouchily rebuff each of her suggestions for alternative forms of entertainment.

'Christ it's depressing sitting in with you like this,' she sighed, exasperated. 'You look like you want to kill yourself.'

'I feel like killing myself,' I replied with a large dose of self-pity, before solemnly explaining my scheme of reparations.

With her usual upbeat positivity, which I couldn't help but find irksome and slightly patronising, she did her best to put an optimistic spin on the situation. But I wasn't open to it and it was a strain just to remain civil. When she took herself off to bed early, I felt a little bad. I knew I was being unfair. It's good to know someone is behind you, but I'm still the one who has to endure the pain.

### Wednesday 6 April, 2005

**10.45 a.m. Work.** Just come out of a team meeting. It was as if somebody had flipped a switch – Mullen and Fell were the most animated I've seen them, barking and clapping like a couple of excited seals as our team leader threw out bits of work. I sat back and let them gobble it all up, content to be left with scraps. These two oddities thrive on a full in-tray. Me, I like to think Parkinson's Law applies – that work expands to fill the time available for its completion.

## Sunday 17 April, 2005

**10.30 p.m. The sofa.** Took off to Brighton for the weekend with Kelly – a burst of spontaneity not accounted for in the spreadsheet of measured existence. Did manage to forget my problems for a few hours. After the pubs, we stumbled down to the beach where we spent hours skimming stones into the sea until our arms hurt. Capped it off with a fry-up at dawn in one of the 24 hr gay cafés. Will just have to add a few extra rows of numbers when I get to work tomorrow; extend the sentence by a few weeks for bad behaviour and pencil in a new release date. Jesus! How did it come to this?

## Monday 18 April, 2005

**8.45 a.m. Office.** Took a calculated risk and submitted my first hooky timesheet – getting creative with my lunch breaks and departure times. Anything to bring those debts down faster. It'd be instant dismissal if I were caught, but I figured I've been here long enough to know people's patterns. Like Mullen. I'm sure that freak is at it too. And he's just the type who'll get away with it – nobody would suspect somebody as conscientious as that.

## Saturday 23 April, 2005

**11.30 a.m. Home.** Go the boy. Took a call earlier from the Rat in Australia. The chief's only decided to sack his debt off – just like that, he's stopped paying.

He asked again when I thought I'd make it over there.

'Not in this decade mate, I'm shelling out over £600 a month at the minute, it's more than I spend on rent,' I said despondently.

'That's fucked,' he said sympathising. 'But you should fuck it off and come over anyway.'

'Easier said than done,' I said, unable to share in his bullishness.

'Listen to this then, it might cheer you up a bit. You remember how I was working like a bitch before I left trying to pay off debt and save up for travelling?'

'Uh-huh.'

'Well, we blew all our savings in Thailand and I caned all the cards again. When we got to Sydney we were fucked, we had to clean the hostel for a week to pay our board. Then we landed the pikiest jobs. I've been working as a fucking bin man.'

I pissed myself laughing: 'Nothing's changed then!' His designated job in our uni household was bin-boy.

'Yeah, I knew you'd like that. Anyway, it was pissing me off, earning Aussie dollars and paying back pounds.'

'Didn't you get any tips? You were always good at it.'

'Fucking listen – twat!'

'Sorry.'

'Then I got chatting to one of our neighbours in Bondi, London geezer, proper wide boy. He told me how he was in exactly the same situation so he thought fuck it, I've got my residency visa, and just stopped paying. That was over a year ago and not a dickie bird. He's not the only one either, couple of his mates have done the same thing. Funniest thing is, he's got shitloads of Australian credit cards.'

'You know I can believe that.'

'So anyway, there I was lying on the beach topping up my tan, thinking of England, which may as well be another fucking planet right now, and I thought *what* am I doing? If they want it back, then they'll just have to come and find me.'

I was laughing. Hearing his tale of rebellion had lifted my spirits. And he wasn't even done.

'It gets better. Barclays rang my mum's house last week and she told them I'd moved to Poland.' He too was cackling down the phone by this point.

Once again he tried to persuade me into booking myself a one-way ticket, which caused me to slip back into gloom mode. It wasn't quite so easy, I explained, there's not just me to think about.

**1.00 p.m.** Keep thinking about Ratboy's shirk. Can't disagree with his logic. What with the geographical and mental distance between himself and his creditors, it does seem absurd to keep sending money back to England. He's also planning to apply for citizenship and says he's never coming back. He's left me with a nice mental image: the Rat on the other side of the world frolicking in the surf, whilst back home, representatives of 'Thug & Sons' are busy knocking on doors in the rain. Not to mention, here I am fretting and struggling, when all it takes is a rucksack and a plane ticket.

**3.00 p.m.** This isn't the only country on earth, a world citizen can live anywhere he cares to call home. And if that somewhere happens to be a place where your creditors can't reach you, then so much the better. It's a romantic notion too, joining the ranks of debt fugitives, one that appeals to my adventurous side. Imagine, assuming a whole new identity and turning up in a town as the mysterious stranger to start a new life. It could be my opportunity for a 'day zero'. Maybe that's what I need: to torch my history and start afresh. My very own 'Day Zero'…

**3.15 p.m.** I think at some time in their life, in one sense or another, most people have wished for a day zero, either to go back to the start of a sequence of events or to have their tally of indiscretions erased.

**Friday 29 April, 2005**
**8.00 p.m. Home.** It's the height of the silly season. Had to

turn down a stag-do to Barcelona in June. Doesn't anybody just go to the pub anymore? And it gets worse. Last week Kelly received an invite from one of her friends – to their wedding in New Zealand of all places. Would not be at all shocked if we didn't get invited to a ceremony on the moon by the time the year's out. Am actually beginning to enjoy turning these people down.

### Monday 2 May, 2005

**8.30 p.m. Home.** Had something of an epiphany in bed last night. Feeling the frustrations of another fleeting weekend and racked with Sunday dread, I suddenly struck upon the ingenious plan of photocopying books so I could read at my desk without attracting attention. I was already congratulating myself during my morning commute, thinking I'd hit upon the perfect solution to enable me to get something out of the working day.

I arrived in good humour for a change, immediately setting about preparing my pamphlet at the Xerox machine. Smiling at my own ingenuity, I made myself a mug of hot tea before settling down to enjoy a furtive read. Mullen was engrossed in his report, staring gormlessly into his screen and tapping his pen on his teeth. He'd stay like that until lunchtime, rather like an installation art piece or an actor hired to remain in pose. Glancing over my shoulder, Fell was similarly preoccupied, his plump head bowed in monastic dedication.

I commenced my own meditation, working my way through my photocopied booklet, '*On the Shortness of Life*' by the Roman philosopher Seneca. He writes that we complain about the briefness of human existence, but the problem is not that we have a short time to live, but that we waste a lot of it, treating time as our least valuable commodity. He tells us that we have ample time for a rewarding life and for 'high achievement' if we use it well – in other words, if we have time for ourselves.

Despite the poverty of my surroundings, I was enjoying the tutorial and had taken to marking my favourite passages with a highlighter. In my head I was somewhere in ancient Rome, sprawled on the lawn of a sunny villa with the wind on my face, contemplating questions of mortality, when I suddenly felt the sharp jolt of the present. Aware of a presence behind me, I looked up to see Chris Fell beside my chair, his flabby frame and stern, revolted expression awaiting my attention.

It would've been worse to try and cover up, and I turned around to engage with him, hoping he wouldn't notice. I couldn't help but wear a guilty expression, and felt disgusted with myself for being in thrall to this oaf as he proceeded to inform me about a new project. It was a 'drop everything' assignment – one of the councillors had been on the line, demanding an urgent report. I could almost make out the puppet strings attached to Fell's shirt sleeves as he explained things. I had to visit the archives and without being too conspicuous, I slid a file over Seneca as I left the room.

I returned to find a post-it note stuck to my keyboard. It was from the boss requesting 'a quick word in private'. After the dressing down – which comprised a lecture to the effect that 'this isn't a library, if you want to read go to college…' – I had to suffer the further indignity of returning to sit with the traitor. I must've imagined a mobster's entire repertoire of smart lines and violent punishments for the creeping little cake-scoffer as I walked back down the corridor. I had a choice: either confront him or remain quiet and keep my job. So I sat smarting, consumed with impotent rage, unable to concentrate as I visualised myself swinging Fell around the room by the knot of his tie.

It was a long, painful afternoon. I refused, or was unable to make eye contact with anyone. I couldn't think about anything else. I kept imagining the whistle-blowing conference during my absence, picturing a triumphant Fell squeaking back to his desk to await my return. I looked down and noticed that my fists were clenched and my knuckles white. It may have been paranoia, but the usually solitary Mullen kept approaching Fell to discuss a host of issues. I had the impression these two had somehow bonded over my humiliation and I left for the day feeling crushed and ruined.

I couldn't bring myself to relay the episode to Kelly. To repeat it would be to paint a picture of pathetic powerlessness. Had to make out I had indigestion when she caught me pulling faces at the ceiling.

**Thursday 5 May, 2005**
**11.45 a.m. Work.** Since the events of Monday, the relationship between myself and Fell is best described as one of mutual contempt. It's at least a more honest situation. Neither of us need pretend anymore and I'm holding firm in our little game of 'who blinks first' when we pass in the corridor. Mercifully, I'm able to sit with my back to him the rest of the time. Only in the arena of the workplace can such creatures thrive, only in this sphere can the strong suffer at hands of the weak.

## Monday 9 May, 2005

**10.45 a.m. Office.** And in darkness there is light. Walked into the toilets earlier and saw Fell's instantly recognisable plastic dork shoes poking out under the stall. Without a moment's hesitation, I hit the light switch and backed out the door, hearing a muffled cry of consternation as it closed behind me.

Revelling in my handiwork and quick thinking as I awaited Fell's return, it took everything I had to disguise my convulsions from Mullen, even stuffing my head in my drawer at one point, as I visualised Fell with his breeks around his ankles huffily wiping up in the dark. When he reappeared ten minutes later, I kept my eyes firmly fixed on my screen, biting down on my bottom lip to keep from exploding. Small but potent victory.

## Tuesday 10 May, 2005

**11.30 a.m. Office.** Should've known it would come back to bite me. Thanks to Fell, I've been saddled with a huge project. The deadshit had the gall to propose me as lead officer on a massive estate regeneration scheme during our work-programming meeting. I couldn't really protest and had to swallow it. The only thing I could do to maintain my dignity was to keep my eyes fixed on the boss during the conversation to signal to Fell that I didn't acknowledge his existence. You always lose in the end – the hierarchy of the weak makes sure of that.

**2.30 p.m. Office.** Ducked into Book Mongers at lunch to try and lift myself. Bought a beautiful soft-cover John Fante novel, which sparked a spate of passionate raving about the imprint. The guys working in there have got it right. All day surrounded by books, reading books, talking books. What a life.

**2.45 p.m.** That little visit has only increased my torment, triggering a spell of melancholic envy. Life can be so unfair at times. Jobs like that aren't an option for heavily indebted fools. I suppose a fraudulent bastard like me gets what he deserves.

### Thursday 12 May, 2005
**11.15 a.m. Office.** Saw an advert on the tube this morning for a Virgin credit card with an introductory 0% interest rate on balance transfers for nine months. Applied online over my first cup of tea to take advantage of the special rate.

### Monday 23 May, 2005
**8.00 p.m. Home.** Virgin card activated with half the balance shifted from Mint card.

# Spitting in the Dark

*'A penny's worth of tears will not settle a pound's worth of debt.'*

Old Proverb

Tuesday 2 August, 2005

**10.00 a.m. Office.** I should be pleased. I've managed to clear the Mint card, but it's a trifling amount compared to the other debts. According to the *Ten Point Action Plan for Getting Yourself Out of Debt*, which I cut out of the Sunday paper, paying off the smallest debt first is supposed to make you feel 'good' and 'positive' about making progress. Well, I feel like topping myself or doing a bunk. Who writes this shit? I'll bet none of these journalists have ever saddled themselves with my kind of debt. Quite frankly, the prospect of confronting the remainder of my debts fills me with total despair. I can't see myself ever being rid of them.

**10.30 a.m.** My efforts have hardly made a jot of difference, the final total's still hopelessly insurmountable. It's a wonder I can still get out of bed in the morning. There's no way I'll be able to endure this stinking job long enough without going insane. A few more years of this and I'll be the one carrying out the dirty protests in the toilets. On the point of booking myself in at the doc's to get some happy pills.

**11.00 a.m.** What a state I'm in. I blame myself for being so reckless, but I'm also angry with the bank for allowing me to repeatedly max out and consolidate. They kept on feeding me until I'd stuffed myself to the point where I could no longer move. I feel weak for trying to shift the burden of responsibility, but fuck it – they knew how much I was earning. They coax you into their cynically devised trap and once they've got you where they want you, they suck away at you like a leech, draining all your vitality.

That's why they've made it easier than it's ever been. Why you don't even have to go and see them anymore, why there's no intimidating cross-examination; you simply pick up the phone or if you prefer no contact at all, then you apply online. It's all so faceless now. Gone are the days when you had to actually demonstrate a worthwhile need for the money. Nowadays they're bombarding you with adverts imploring you to spend. I'll bet if I picked up the phone and called them right now they'd be all: 'how much do you want Mr Livingson... I can do that today for you if you like, Mr Livingson...'

One thing's for sure: somebody's getting rich off my misery.

**3.00 p.m.** Well, since the situation's so hopeless anyway... booked a weekend in Rome next month for Kelly's birthday.

**11.30 p.m.** We're definitely going through a rocky patch. Holidays to Rome aren't the answer. Halfway through a bottle of wine earlier, Kelly broke down. She says she doesn't recognise me anymore, that I'm not the man she met. That hurt. It hurt because I know it's true. No denying I've been depressed. Staying in, reading, keeping to myself. Tried to reassure her I'm still in here somewhere. Don't know how convincing I was, even I can't be sure I'm still around. You try and keep your pecker up and put on a brave face but I'm only ever pretending.

**Wednesday 3 August, 2005**
**11.30 a.m. Work.** Kelly was looking at me strangely when I came out of the shower this morning.

'Why are you looking at me like that?' I scowled defensively. I thought I must have a humungous spot somewhere on my face.

'You don't remember spitting?' she said irritably, pointing her hairbrush at me.

'*Spitting?*'

'Don't tell me you don't remember…' she said, with a troubled look on her face. 'Me shaking you awake? To tell you to stop spitting?'

'I wasn't spitting,' I insisted, getting agitated. This was a ridiculous allegation to be facing before breakfast. I began throwing on my clothes without even drying off.

'*Yes you were!*' she cried forcibly. 'You were driving me mad with your constant fidgeting, *then* you started spitting!'

I looked at her blankly. I felt like I was in the dock, having committed a murder I had no recollection of.

'You were spitting in your sleep!' she said crossly. 'You were leaning over the side of the bed, hacking and spitting. It was fucked up! You kept doing it and were trying to say something, but I couldn't make sense of it.'

I had no memory of this whatsoever. I wanted her to tell me she was joking. I left for work feeling a little shaken. I didn't much like that look on her face either. It was most unsettling. I've felt weird all morning. Spitting, of all things.

### Friday 5 August, 2005

**7.30 p.m. Home.** The tension in our flat is almost unbearable. I can feel Kelly watching me all the time, which only makes me more irritable. I've noticed she's been going out a lot more, no doubt to get away from me. I can feel the distance between us increasing. Everything's turned sour and I feel like it's unravelling. I'm not enjoying this relationship anymore and neither is Kelly. I know she's been trying to reach out to me, but something inside is preventing me from responding.

**12.15 a.m.** Kelly's in bed sleeping soundly and I'm staring at the walls with only my troubled mind for company. This can't go on. I'm close to breaking point. I'm slowly ruining our relationship, sucking the joy out of it. The pressure's too great. Maybe it would be better if I were on my own. I'm dragging her down with me.

**Monday 8 August, 2005**
**10.30 a.m. Work.** Battling with a major hangover this morning. Drank two coffees in succession on the way here to try and get on top of it, but that just made it worse. I've got the shakes as well, looking at my screen's giving me a headache.

**2.30 p.m.** Had enough of wrestling with the spinning head and found myself heading to the pub at lunchtime. It was all I could think to do to take the edge off, to sink a couple of pints. Ignoring the trendy upmarket places along the main drag, I opted for a quiet back-street venue.

Ended up in a proper drinker's den, a tight kip the size of someone's front room and save for the presence of the bar, decked out exactly like one. Each of the small, tightly packed tables were occupied by solo drinkers, men sitting opposite an empty chair, staring into their glasses or vacantly at the faded Constable prints screwed to the walls. It was a particularly miserable scene. A lot of tense faces with an air of desperation about them – people seeking refuge from their lives. Despite being almost full, it was incredibly quiet.

The loudest sound was that of the fruit machine spinning, bleeping and occasionally spewing out coins. Lost in their own thoughts, nobody bothered anyone else.

Of course it was the antithesis of the chalkboard gastro pub, packets of peanuts and crisps being the full extent of the menu.

Strangely, I didn't seem to mind as I consumed my very first liquid lunch. Although I felt like a bit of a freak upon my return; called over by my boss Des Crown to run through my report, I opened my mouth to speak and unleashed a wave of beer fumes in his direction. I took a cautious step back, hoping he hadn't noticed.

**8.00 p.m. Home**. As I walked up to the front door of our building, I could see nobody was home. Didn't think much of it. Assumed she was out after work again, that she'd forgotten to call. Then I saw it on the kitchen table – the note.

She needs some time to think, she says, 'space' as she put it. *Space:* the death knell of a relationship.

She hasn't even told me where she's staying, just 'a friend's place' for a few days. Of course I couldn't get through. It was the first thing I did. I had to listen to her breezy phone message laced with flirtation, picturing her there, sitting in the company of this nameless 'friend'.

**9.00 p.m.** Have read the letter countless times, analysing each line to try to interpret the meaning of every word. She hasn't said 'it's over', she's not saying that. At least not yet. But it's the 'space' thing that really worries me. 'Space' is dangerous, it's a void of uncertainty where momentous decisions can be made. Is that what she needs the room for, to decide whether it's worth continuing?

No, she hasn't said 'this is it', that she's leaving me for good. I have to hold on to that. That at least is something. But this is a mess. And I have only myself to blame.

She's said she'll be in touch in a few days. I'll have to endure a few agonising days until I hear from her. I wish I could speak to her now, more than anything I just want to talk to her, to see her face.

**10.25 p.m.** I'm embarrassed to think of my girl being forced to flee our home, to escape me. I'm ashamed to think of her out there, pouring out her troubles to somebody, telling them how difficult and unreasonable I've been. I can only look to myself. I'm reaping my own bitter harvest, suffering the humiliation of our intimacy being cut open and dissected, no doubt over a bottle of wine, with murmurs of understanding from a well-intended friend, too many cigarettes, perhaps some tears, a lot of empathy, my issues, undoubtedly my issues.

*'You've been like this for nearly a year now.'* She tried talking to me – several times – but I preferred to slosh around in a sea of self-pity, an indulgence that's resulted in an empty flat and an unanswerable letter. I foolishly ignored her, wallowing in my books and their profound aphorisms on the pain and injustice of existence. Not content with damaging myself, I pulled her down with me.

**11.05 p.m.** Picked up the Monkey Magic photograph from the mantelpiece and felt myself welling up. I remember that day, we were in our element. I'd just moved here. We were invincible, our bond unbreakable. Now I can hardly bear to look at our beaming faces in the picture. I'd give anything to be able to rewind, to be back there again. But it feels like a lifetime away.

### Tuesday 9 August, 2005
**8.38 a.m. Office.** The flat felt unnaturally empty this morning. I missed the noise of the hairdryer, whooshing and roaring as I

battled to stay asleep, the morning news report on the television, several notches too high. The bathroom was cold and unwelcoming without its steamy mirror and damp shower mat. My toast was missing the aftertaste of perfume and I drank my coffee in silence, saving my first words of the day for the bus driver.

**9.12 a.m.** Lay awake for hours last night with a wave of gloomy scenarios running through my head. I kept imagining the worst possible outcomes, seeing myself having to tell people we were finished: *You probably haven't heard, we've split up, I've split up with Kelly… because… well it was me really, I…*

**2.30 p.m.** Been constantly checking my phone in the hope she'll call, even switched it on and off again to make sure it was working properly. When it rang over lunch with a withheld number, I lunged across the desk to grab it like you see in hostage movies when the husband's waiting for the kidnapper to call. Fucking recruitment consultant, 'with news of an exciting opportunity'. Had to listen to some smarmy South African slicker with an artificial interest in my welfare, asking if I was 'happy in my current position'.

**5.00 p.m. Home.** Came home early in the hope that she might be here waiting for me. Looked straight up at our windows as I turned the corner into our street, only to see the curtains still drawn.

**8.45 p.m.** Went for a big walk. Had to get out of the flat. First thing I wanted to do after I got back was to ring her. Almost did but stopped myself. Have to give her room. Don't push it. We're going to be alright. I'm sure we'll be okay, I'll make sure of it.

**11.50 p.m.** It's been a miserable day. Laid off the booze as I don't want to make myself feel any worse. Another sleepless night ahead.

**Wednesday 10 August, 2005**
**8.45 a.m. Office.** Still no contact. Surely she'll call today.

**9.37 a.m.** Trying to immerse myself in work to give my head a break, but it's impossible to concentrate with all this going on. The world feels different. The unintelligible language of these reports I'm attempting to write is more mindless than ever. It's like I'm acting a part on a stage and I'm up on the balcony watching myself.

**4.45 p.m. Home.** Couldn't stick it anymore, took the afternoon off and trekked up to Hackney to see if I couldn't persuade the bank to loosen the shackles a little. I know they're full of shit with all that 'come and talk to us if you're having difficulty paying' spiel, but I had to try. Plus, it would give me something positive to tell Kelly when we eventually speak.

Also reasoned that with a friendly face in Essex boy Daz, I'd have someone I could lean on. My plan was to target him with a spot of bullshit banter, to use his own method to convince him to improve my terms.

I had to wait to be seen. He was busy at his desk with a 30-something couple that were discussing a loan application for their business – a mother-and-baby café and crèche. I had to listen to their nauseating drivel as they twittered on about the cost implications of creating their *twee* little paradise in the inner city. This pair was the embodiment of mindless conformism. The guy, who sat with his MacBook open on his knees, wore a trucker's cap and thick-rimmed designer specs, a grey suit jacket over a T-shirt, distressed jeans and smart trainers of the type found nestling on the shelves of expensive Upper Street boutiques. In her flower-patterned dress and cowgirl boots and hat, his partner looked like she'd arrived straight from Glastonbury.

They were both well-spoken, and I listened in amusement as Daz chatted to them in an affected posh voice to interest them in additional financial products. It brought a smile to my face for the first time this week as I imagined myself interjecting to tell him to pull his thumb out of his arse. For a brief minute, I was delivered from my own troubles.

When they were done, the tedious twins leaving the bank in an excitable fuss, I stood to approach his desk, Darren looking uncomfortable as I nodded at him, returning my greeting with a slightly subdued 'alright geez'. I thought about giving him the 'hullo', but I needed his help, so I started by softening up with a bit of football chat. West Ham were promoted to the Premier League, how did he fancy their chances of making an impact this season? They'd do well, I thought.

I didn't much like having to demean myself by rubbing cocks with this classless clegger, but he was all I had. With no choice but to paint a picture of my miserable existence, I dropped my pants and pleaded for assistance. Nothing doing. Not even an extension of the loan period to reduce the payments. 'When the bank's seen a sustained period of repayment, maybe we can look at restructuring. Come back in six or seven months,' he said frostily, avoiding eye contact with me by looking intently at his screen. What else could be done? Surely there must be something? Nothing. Nothing at all? A shake of the head and a blank expression, followed by an impatient bout of pen-tapping that made me want to slam the sole of my shoe into his face.

He wasn't budging. He'd quickly dropped the matey façade and was now stiff and businesslike. Faced with the choice of degrading myself further in front of this imbecile, I had to take my leave. Angry with myself for betraying my instincts and actually putting some faith in this deceitful little faker, I walked back to the flat in a fury.

**12.15 a.m.** Neighbour just banged on the ceiling, upset by my unsociable housework frenzy. Needed to keep myself occupied, and embarked on a late night spring-clean of the flat.

**Thursday 11 August, 2005**
**11.30 a.m. Office.** Witnessed a scene this morning that was both uplifting and crushing. I could see the police vans at the end of the road as I walked towards the bus stop to begin my commute. As I drew level with the incident, I saw a group of young men standing outside the last house in the street, each looking dishevelled and bleary-eyed, sleeping bags draped over their shoulders and rolled cigarettes hanging out of their mouths. They'd been squatting in the empty building and had just been evicted.

I stopped to observe, full of admiration for their spirit of defiance, their refusal to play the game, to endure shit jobs to pay rent, placing their daily freedom above all material concerns. I stood ruminating on the authenticity of their way of life when one of them looked over at me. As our eyes met, I felt his piercing gaze of derision on me: the regular chump in his sad little uniform. Still looking in my direction, the squatter brushed his curly unkempt mop from his face and spat contemptuously on the ground. I had to look away and move on, the sound of my brogues slapping conspicuously on the pavement as I walked away.

As the bus crawled through the traffic en route to the tube station, with me impatiently looking at my watch, I thought about what I'd just seen. I didn't have to play the game and conform either. Anyone can opt out of the system if they choose to. All it takes is a little conviction.

**4.30 p.m. Home.** For some reason, I was sure she'd call today. Maybe it'll happen tonight. I've done a lot of thinking these past few days. I'm ready to talk… there's a great deal I want to say.

**8.50 p.m.** Still knocking about in the empty void. Have been shouldering this alone, can't bring myself to ring anyone and confess what an idiot I've been.

**12.30 a.m. Home.** Been pacing around the room like a mental patient. It's madness. I've allowed the girl I love to drift away, maybe throwing away the best thing that's ever happened to me, and for what? Because of debt, because of *banks*.

**12.50 a.m.** I'm not doing this anymore. Fuck debt and fuck banks.

### Friday 12 August, 2005
**8.45 a.m. Office.** Charged into work this morning feeling mad and defiant, strutting along the pavements with my elbows out and shoulders square, daring anyone to step in my way. I've

allowed myself to be pushed around for too long, cowering and meekly accepting when I should've been standing tall and fighting. How much more desperate do things need to become? No, things are going to be different from now on. I feel like the floored fighter who's just gotten to his feet to beat the count. I have the gloves on, ready to throw a few punches.

Arriving at the office I wasted no time in commencing my research. If it's not an option, I need to know so I can rule it out immediately and move on. In our one-click world, the answers are only ever a page away.

**Bankruptcy is one way of dealing with debts you cannot pay. Bankruptcy proceedings:**

**– free you from overwhelming debts so you can make a fresh start, subject to some restrictions; and**
**– make sure your assets are shared out fairly among your creditors.**

**Anyone can go bankrupt, including individual members of a partnership. There are different insolvency procedures for dealing with companies and for partnerships themselves.**

**12.30 p.m. Office.** Finally. She called. She's asked me to meet her tonight at the pub in Wood Green, the place where we spent so many happy evenings back when things were less complicated.

# Choose Life

'*That some person is genius enough not to pay his debt, that at least is something one hears of now and then; why shouldn't a state be able to do the same if only all are agreed?*'

Søren Kierkegaard

Tuesday 16 August, 2005

**1.30 p.m. Marazion Beach, Cornwall.** Stretched out on my towel in the sun facing the sea. Kelly's in the water beckoning to me. She's trying to make out it's not cold, I'll wait till she's got her shoulders under before I believe her. It's been a good couple of days. A world away from the claustrophobic confines of our flat. We're both where we should be, 'on the sick', and it feels just like old times again. Well, almost.

We left early the morning after she called. We felt like a couple of 16-year-olds running off to Gretna Green for a shotgun wedding, as we boarded the train at Paddington. Since we pitched up at the campsite, it's been pure relaxation. A bout of mindless fun after the heaviness. We're not there yet though. It'll take time. And I'm not fully restored to myself, but I'm feeling a little better, although there's much to do, and a lot to investigate.

Monday 22 August, 2005

**10.30 a.m. Office.** Returned to work feeling refreshed. Was only away for a week but I found I had forgotten my log-in details and had to phone IT for a reminder. Sometimes a man needs time and space in which to think, to look out at the ocean and walk across the land, to be able to realise the true nature of things. Of what significance are one man's troubles against a backdrop of rock formations and land masses millions of years old? When confronted with the great expanse of the world, away from the narrow corridors of daily life, the mind opens up to new possibilities.

**11.00 a.m.** Nothing is certain, but bankruptcy is starting to make sense. The quickest way out of this mess, and a final goodbye to those debts. They'll be written off and I'll be able to make a fresh start after one year.

**11.05 a.m.** It's difficult to imagine, difficult to comprehend that it's come to this. But I have to imagine it. All other options are unworkable.

**11.10 a.m.** But are my choices really as limited as I've believed them to be? After all, man is always free to choose, as Sartre said. We are, he asserted, always free to negate our situation and try to change it.

**11.15 a.m.** All week, while we were in Cornwall, I walked around carrying a batch of crumpled articles and Fact Sheets with me, pulling them out on the beach or surreptitiously in the pub, re-reading the pros and cons of it all. Of course they warn against it being the easy option, they tell you that you'll lose all your assets, that it'll cost more to borrow in the future, that your bankruptcy stays on your credit file for six years. But there's little point in trying to preserve my financial standing when everything else is falling apart, including and especially me.

**11.20 a.m.** It looks good on paper, but it's another thing to actually go through with it. And *I* have to do it – I have to file my own bankruptcy petition. It's a huge step to take, an irreversible leap off a cliff into the unknown. I have to make sure I know what I'm doing.

**11.45 a.m.** As I explained my bankruptcy plan to Kelly, to her credit, she didn't recoil in horror, but remained calm and rational as we talked it through. She wants me back, she said, and if that's what it takes, then she'll support me in whatever I choose to do. Although understandably I could tell she was more than a little apprehensive about it. She asked me a lot of questions, many of which I was unable to answer. Did I have the nerve to see it through? Would I tell anyone? How would it affect her?

We agreed not to discuss it until I knew more. I realise how lucky I am to have her, just the mere mention of the word 'bankruptcy' would see most women packing their status anxieties into their Gucci handbags and heading for the hills. Which makes me wonder, is bankruptcy the ultimate taboo of a materialist society?

Then again, bankruptcy is the optimum state for those who want to see a new world order and bring down the system. That's right. I'm not really a banal *work-consume* drone on the verge of financial meltdown, quite the opposite in fact. I'm Comandante PJ Livingson, enemy of the profit margin and future leader of the new revolution, the bloodless uprising that history will remember as the movement that brought the banks to their knees and saw the end of global capitalism.

Well, anyone can dream.

### Saturday 27 August, 2005
**9.30 p.m. Home.** At the studios earlier with Kelly's band, as they laid down the tracks for their new album. Spent a good hour in the pub with Richie, an anarchist Scot and chief songwriter for the group. It's a mark of a man's good character if you struggle to picture him in a shirt and tie. I've always been envious of the way he's lived his life. Purely for art and good times. A truly authentic individual.

The subject soon came round to my debt problem. I told him how I'd screwed myself.

'Man, that's some millstone around your neck, it's stopping you from living.'

'I know, I think about it every day. It follows me about like a black cloud. Every time I think about something I want to do, it always comes back to it, the same question – but what about my debts, how will I pay them? It nearly ended my relationship with Kelly. I was no fun to live with.'

'You should speak to Citizens Advice, they'll know what to do.'

'I know, I know, you're not the first person to say that. Should've done it a long time ago.'

'If I was in your situation, that's the first thing I'd have done. Right now you're laying out some serious money and going nowhere fast.'

'Tell me about it, it's killing me. Although I think I've hit on an escape plan. I'm actually thinking about bankruptcy. I've started to read up on it.'

I felt safe telling him. From what I knew of his history, Richie was the type of person you could trust.

'I was actually gonna suggest that too. I think that's what Citizens Advice will tell you as well.'

'I've done a lot of thinking about it, and there's no way I'm paying all that back. It'll take me years, and I'll be a broken man at the end of it, there'll be nothing left except an empty shell.'

He looked at me and grimaced.

'Fuckin' banks,' I snapped. 'They need to be taught a lesson. They can sing for it. Nothing would give me greater pleasure than knowing they've had to write it off.'

'That's the spirit,' he said, becoming animated. 'Tell 'em to go fuck themselves. So what if they blacklist you? But what about your job? You can't go bankrupt if you're able to make the payments, right?'

'I think I know how to take care of that,' I said conspiratorially, shifting my chair closer to him and lowering my voice. 'I'll need to create the right conditions. A little period of manufactured unemployment should do the trick.'

Richie smiled at me approvingly. 'That'd be one slick manoeuvre. Think you've got the balls to pull it off?'

I skulled the remainder of my beer and slid my glass across the table as we both got up to leave.

'We'll see, won't we?'

# A Citizen Advised

*'It could take 77 years on average for people contacting Citizens Advice to get out of the red… people are condemned to a lifetime of poverty burdened by debt'.*

Citizens Advice Bureau Report, 2007

**Monday 19 September, 2005**

**8.55 a.m. Office.** The madness continues: Mint have increased my credit limit as a reward for paying off my balance. They've also sent me six grand's worth of credit card cheques.

**3.30 p.m. Office.** Amused myself by spending the last hour searching for famous bankrupts. If the likes of Mark Twain, Daniel Defoe and Raymond Carver have been through it, then perhaps it's a necessary rite of passage for the aspiring artist? You're nothing unless you've gone bankrupt.

**Monday 17 October, 2005**

**10.30 p.m. Home.** Back from the final fling in Rome. Had been trying to keep the cost down but then thought, fuck it, if I do eventually go bankrupt, I may as well spend the bank's money. Mint card's probably back to where it was before, or worse…

**Friday 21 October, 2005**

**2.15 p.m. Work.** Logged into the Mint account for confirmation that almost a year into my debt recovery attempt, I'm exactly where I started. The writing's on the wall.

**Sunday 30 October, 2005**

**5.30 p.m. Home.** I wish we'd stayed home. After his sneering and gloating, I am under no illusions as to what my father would make of his son, the 'bankrupt'. We'd taken him up on his offer of a couple of days in the Cotswolds, visiting him and Jan at the caravan park where they'd booked an out of season break.

We arrived late on Friday, and they were already in the clubhouse, watching the evening's entertainment: a blaring talent show for the under 15s, MC'd by a camp young blond fellow with ridiculously red cheeks. It was like watching a live pilot for X-Factor and no less excruciating. After the show had ended and the excitable host had finally stopped shrieking into the microphone, we were able to talk. Everything was going fine until I mentioned an old name from his past, someone my mum had over her place recently.

'Tony de Souza?' he said sneering.

'Yeah that's him,' I nodded.

'A right flash git, used to lord it over us like he owned the town. A proper show-off, with his sports cars and swimming pool. But he didn't impress me. Nah, never had any time for him.'

'So you didn't like him then?' I said jokingly.

'You may laugh,' he said, aware that we were laughing at him, 'but it was all built on sand.' His tone gained an air of triumphant relish. 'His business folded and he ended up bankrupt, didn't he. They took everything.' He spoke smugly, making no attempt to conceal his gloating.

I couldn't look at Kelly. Hearing that word come out of my father's mouth was like a punch in the gut. I sat and listened with an unbearable tightness in my stomach as he carried on rejoicing in the other man's misfortune.

'He ended up in a Council house for a while, ringing around, begging people for work. Hah! Humiliating. The whole town knew. Everyone knew he was a bankrupt. You make a big show of it when you've got it – it'll be big news when you lose it too. Ah, the humiliation. A bankrupt.'

It was the way he kept saying 'humiliation' and 'bankrupt' that unnerved me – savouring the words like they were a delicious steak or a swig of red wine. I was totally rattled and had to escape to the bar, with Kelly quickly following behind.

We stayed the night in their chalet and thankfully there was no more talk of disgraced bankrupts.

**10.30 p.m.** Not that I ever had any intention of telling the old fella, but thanks to him, my bankruptcy bravado has taken a severe battering. Considering the story of my life so far has only caused my confidence to plummet further. I've never made any big decisions. They've all been easy. It was an easy choice to follow the university path after school, and just as straightforward to utilise my education to embark on a career. My path has been perfectly conventional. Am I capable of breaking with the easy normalcy of my life? Or will I end up like Dad's old nemesis, broken and ruined?

For almost six years I've been working. I have a home and rent to pay. There is a set and established order to my life. Can I really break from the regular by doing something totally irregular? Do I possess the gumption to ditch my job and live out on the edge for a while? And do I have the guts to stand up in court and make an unequivocal and irreversible declaration?

Again I think about my father. Financial ruin would be anathema to him, the ultimate unspeakable shame to be avoided at all costs. To willingly choose it would be madness in his eyes. But he's a man of convention and happy to be so. He likes and admires the established orthodoxy. His horizons don't extend beyond the driveway.

**11.30 p.m.** Dragged myself off to bed, heavy with doubt, as all these thoughts and challenges churned around in my head. In the darkness of the room, I could make out the outline of my work shirt on its hanger, hooked on the wardrobe door, ready for the morning. Tomorrow was another day at work, another well-structured, unimaginative and tightly defined day in my life. A day like any of the thousands of days that had gone before.

**Monday 31 July, 2006**
**9.20 a.m. Home.** If I don't act now, I never will. I *will* do something about those debts – have taken the morning off work to finally call Citizens Advice.

**9.40 a.m.** That's it? I can't believe how casual she was about it. The woman from Citizens Advice has just confirmed my suspicions: bankruptcy is the answer, the quick-fix solution to end the nightmare.

'Hello, is that Citizens Advice? I'd like to talk to someone about my debts.'

'Well you can speak with me, how much are we talking about?' Straight down to business. I told her the total. 'Well, that's a considerable amount, although not uncommon. Do you have any intention of applying for a mortgage in the near future?'

'Absolutely none,' I said emphatically. 'I've had enough of debt to last me a lifetime.'

'Have you considered bankruptcy?' she said easily. In fact, her nonchalance was such that I had a mental image of a woman chewing gum, filing her nails and doing the crossword as she spoke with me.

'Yes, that's the main reason I'm calling.'

'Well everybody's doing it, with your debts I'd say that's the best option.'

Just like that, everybody's doing it, jump onboard.

'That's what I've been thinking. The problem is I earn a good salary. At the moment, I'm able to service my debts quite well, but I hate my job. I'm sure I'll have had a breakdown before I get anywhere close to paying it all off. You see, I was thinking of quitting and getting a job that just covers the rent.' As I heard myself speak, I realised that all I really wanted was somebody to agree with me and tell me my plan was sound. 'That sounds like the best way to go about it. Good luck.'

And with that, the call ended, rather abruptly, but there was nothing else to say.

Bankruptcy – everybody's doing it.

**Friday 4 August, 2006**
**10.20 a.m. Office.** Today's headline: 'RECORD NUMBERS GO BANKRUPT.'

Stopped dead in my tracks as I passed the paper kiosk outside the station and saw it. Sat on the tube and read the article twice over. Apparently more than 26,000 people became insolvent in the second quarter of this year. That's 26,000 souls who're free from the shackles of debt. Inked my name on the timesheet this morning thinking, *what the fuck am I doing coming in here?*

**12.30 p.m.** Got the bit between my teeth now. Inspired by this morning's news, have spent last three hours reading up on the UK debt crisis. The Insolvency Service website's a veritable feast of information, the statistics showing that bankruptcy is on the rise and increasing at an alarming rate. Experts are even predicting 100,000 individual insolvencies by the end of the year, a record by some distance. Has the fuse on that time bomb been lit?

**2.30 p.m.** Printed out another Fact-Sheet on the pros and cons of bankruptcy and sat poring over it.

## ADVANTAGES

– When the bankruptcy order is over you can make a fresh start, but this can be after only one year.

– Creditors have to stop most types of court action to get their money back following a bankruptcy order.

– You are allowed to keep certain things, like household goods and a reasonable amount to live on.

– The money you owe can use usually be written off.

## DISADVANTAGES

– It will cost you money (up to £475) to go bankrupt .

– While you are bankrupt, you can't apply for more credit.

– If you own your own home, it might have to be sold (but you may be able to apply to your local authority for re-housing).

– Some of your possessions may have to be sold, for example, you will usually lose your car and any luxury items you own.

– Some professions don't let people who have been made bankrupt carry on working.

– Going bankrupt can affect your immigration status.

– You cannot keep your bankruptcy private. it may be published in your local newspaper.

**3.40 p.m. Office.** Damn my dithering. It's so obvious bankruptcy is the thing for me. My creditors won't be able to touch me and I can make a fresh start in a matter of months. I have no assets and no luxury items, so I have nothing to lose. I wonder how many other debtors are aware that you can just turn your back on all of it and walk away? It's as easy as saying 'no' to debt and 'yes' to life.

**4.00 p.m.** It's funny, on one hand we've never had it so bad in terms of mass indebtedness, but at the same time we've never had it so good in terms of auspicious bankruptcy laws. It certainly never used to be so easy. Not so long ago, bankruptcy was a serious thing, you'd be well and truly shafted for some seven years. So it's a classic case of exploiting the conditions while they remain favourable.

# Can't Pay, Won't Pay

*'The repayment ethic is central to a responsible society. Any
weakening of this ethic would be unwelcome.'*

Malcolm Hurlston,
Chairman of the Consumer Credit Counselling Service, 2007

**Sunday 6 August, 2006**

**12.35 p.m.** Almost choked on my cornflakes this morning. Cracked open the Sunday rag to be met with another state-of-the-nation debt article beneath a suitably alarmist headline: 'ONE PERSON ENTERING INSOLVENCY EVERY MINUTE.' One person every minute – that's some serious default momentum. The cautious columnists and experts have got it wrong. Bankruptcy *is* a 'get out of jail free' card, and one which thousands of people are playing. I intend to be one of them.

**8.30 p.m.** Picked up the paper again. This time a piece in the Comment & Analysis section. A leading British intellectual is proposing a radical idea for abolishing third world debt. He says that instead of waiting for the big Western banks to reduce or cancel the repayments which cripple their economies and ensure they remain in the debt trap, all the debtor countries should join forces and agree to simultaneously default on repayments. After all, he says, what could the International Monetary Fund or the World Bank do in response to a such a widespread, unified default, invade *all* of these countries?

This gets me to thinking that the same logic could just as easily be applied to mass indebtedness in Britain, where millions of individuals are enslaved to banks. Let us unite in our non-payment and have ourselves a mass default revolution. Enough is enough; it's time the people fought back. If the government won't protect us from the banks then we must take it upon ourselves to deliver the message: you've fucked around with us for too long. We'll walk away with our freedom, leaving the shareholders of Great Britain PLC to pick up the pieces and fight amongst themselves.

Ah, the thought of it – people tearing up credit agreements in their thousands, leaving the usurers to mourn their lost profits, the financial centres engulfed by a million fragments of discarded bills blowing through the air. Fuck the useless self-help books and their monastic solutions, the genius is in not paying. I'm sure of it, default is *the only viable solution* for those who desire immediate freedom.

**Monday 7 August, 2006.**

**10.05 a.m. Office.** *One person insolvent for every minute of the day.* It's impossible to ignore something like that when you're clocking in for another week of spirit-crushing tedium. They're out there now, the plucky ones, down at the courthouses handing in their petitions and walking away with their freedom. 65 of them to be precise, going by my clock. At the end of the day five hundred souls will be free from debt misery. It's time to join the bankruptcy bash.

**Wednesday 9 August, 2006**

**10.15 a.m. Office.** No more talking. Have begun creating the conditions for my escape. Starting with a call to EGG to take advantage of their three-month payment holiday. When the woman on the phone asked why I wanted the payment break, I could hardly contain myself. 'I'm saving to go bankrupt,' was what I wanted to say. Held my tongue though, and the arrangements were made. Can now reapportion the money I would've paid to them into my bankruptcy fund. Now that's my kind of accountancy.

**10.30 a.m.** It's happening. Finally, I've taken the first step and it really is happening. I'm walking a new path, my own path. Can't turn back now, have to keep the momentum and see it through.

**10.40 a.m.** Feeling good. After my earlier stunt, I'm filled with a brilliant, beautiful feeling of resolve. I can do it, I can definitely do it.

**Friday 11 August, 2006**
**9.45 a.m. Office.** Decided to stop paying the Virgin card. That's another £100 a month I can stash away in my pillowcase. Plan to stockpile enough money to see me through my period of unemployment.

**10.00 a.m.** Ahhh, if I'd known it was going to be this much fun... All this debt-dodging makes me feel like I'm a member of a resistance movement, plotting and scheming in readiness for an imminent insurgency.

**10.15 a.m.** I'm not imagining it; everywhere I turn I'm finding more evidence of people saying 'no' to debt. The BBC reports this morning on a crucial shift in the nature of bankruptcy petitions; the proportion of bankruptcy petitions from creditors is falling and debtor petitions are on the rise – in other words people are *choosing* bankruptcy for themselves, rather than being forced into it.

**11.30 p.m. Home.** Went to see Kelly's band earlier. Told Richie about my preparations after the show.

'It's premeditated bankruptcy,' I said. 'I've taken a payment break with EGG and I've stopped paying one of the cards.'

'Premeditated bankruptcy, I like it,' he said chuckling. 'You're really going through with it aren't you? I thought you'd bottled it?'

'No way, just you watch me go. I'm taking my life back.'

### Wednesday 23 August, 2006

**7.30 p.m. Home.** Kelly's band had a talent scout come and see their gig a couple of weeks ago. Riche called with the bad news, the feedback being 'they didn't fit the kind of profile the record company were looking for'. Kelly was fairly philosophical about it. 'To be honest,' she said, 'I've no interest in becoming famous, I just want to earn a living out of doing what I love.'

I was impressed by her maturity. She just wants to do something meaningful with her day. I think this is the source of much of the discontent in our society; too many talented people doing pointless jobs, getting worn down by the frustration and meaninglessness of it all. More power to her though – she's not beaten yet. She's going to use this as a spur, saying she plans to explore using her talents in other ways.

### Thursday 24 August, 2006

**11.05 a.m. Doormat.** Letter from Virgin informing me that my payment is overdue and a late payment charge of £25 has been added to my account. Hah! Let them add as many charges as they like, I won't be paying any.

### Monday 4 September, 2006

**1.56 p.m. Office.** The chase is on. Taking a stroll through the park after lunch, I answered my phone to a garbled voice on a bad line asking me for my personal details. I asked him what his business was.

'I'm calling from MBNA about your overdue account. Can you confirm your name and address for security purposes?'

I hung up. As far as I'm aware, I've no business with MBNA.

**7.45 p.m. Home.** Made the mistake of telling Kelly about the call, which made her stress about bailiffs breaking down our door.

'Calm down,' I said after she'd bombarded me with anxious questions. 'They don't send them round if you're a day late, it takes months to get to that stage.'

'Yeah,' she said worriedly. 'But they're calling you already. That's hardly a good sign?'

'It's the first stage of a long process. Don't worry about it.'

She didn't share my confidence, and the only way of calming her down and getting her to drop it was to promise to pay up if they did come round.

### Thursday 7 September, 2006

**10.40 a.m. Office.** Virgin, MBNA, or whatever they call themselves, keep ringing me about my overdue account. Turns out that the hundreds of brands of cards on the market are in fact issued by the same few lenders. Anyway, recognising the number now, I'm ignoring their calls. But boy, are they persistent. The constant ringing of the phone is mightily irritating. Looks like a case of attrition – just have to bed myself in.

### Friday 15 September, 2006

**9.30 a.m. Work.** I'm actually going through with it. Just handed in my notice.

**10.15 a.m.** That's the formalities out of the way. After the obligatory chat with the boss, I charged down the corridor, unable to contain myself. Bundled straight into a meeting room to ring Kelly with the good news. She was a little overwhelmed but I could hear the relief in her voice. No question about it – I'm on my way back. Looking forward to getting home tonight so I can tell her that 'ole Jonny-gonna-do, he don't a-live here no more'. Yea-ha!

**3.30 p.m.** Ah, the office grapevine. Throughout the day, people have been asking where I'm going, expecting news of a better job or an exciting travel itinerary. Hadn't crossed my mind to prepare a story. Imagine the look on their faces if I'd told the truth...

'Where are you off to then?'

'Oh, I'm leaving to go bankrupt.'

Not exactly your conventional resignation, but then I'm through with convention. Fudged it and told them I'm taking a career break. A very long one.

**4.45 p.m.** Ah, to be able to look around at this dreary environment knowing I'm counting down the days never to return. No more drudgery. I'm getting out of here. And in a few weeks I'll be debt free.

### Monday 18 September, 2006
**10.39 a.m. Office.** They've stepped it up a level. My Virgin account's been passed on to their collections department. Got caught out, as I didn't recognise the new number. Hung up mid-sentence, must've been a fault on the line. And there'll be no more letters on my doormat either. We moved house last week and I've neglected to inform them of my change of address, an administrative oversight. I'm sure they'll understand.

### Friday 22 September, 2006
**4.57 p.m. Office.** It's the end of the week and I've had at least 20 calls from the collections department in the last five days. These boys are relentless. And their tactics are simple: persistence, persistence, persistence. The idea being: whoever calls most frequently, gets paid first. But seriously, the constant calling could really fuck with a man's mind. When I'm done with this I might start up a seminar for beleaguered debtors.

LESSON ONE: 'Dealing with Debt Collectors – Why Their Bark is Worse Than Their Bite.'

*'Right class, for our first exercise today, I want you to imagine the person on the other end of the line: picture their cheap shirt and tie, their poor complexion... Can you see the computer screen in front of them? Now concentrate, try to evoke in your mind an image of the poorly lit room in which they spend their dreary days. Consider their miserable existence, reduced to doing this kind of dirty work for global financial institutions. These people are morally bankrupt, they've sold out and you must remember that you are superior to them. Feel better? Now for some role-play, who'd like to volunteer?'*

**Wednesday 27 September, 2006**
**10.30 a.m. Office.** The headlines keep coming: 'BRITAIN RESPONSIBLE FOR A THIRD OF ALL UNSECURED DEBT IN EUROPE'.

Wow. Has she overloaded herself to the point where she might capsize and sink? No doubt the government will dismiss this and bang on about how the economy's in rude health. But it's clear to anyone that the boom time has been built on spending fuelled by debt. Debt that will eventually have to be repaid.

**Saturday 30 September, 2006**
**2.30 p.m. Home.** Called round to our old flat this morning to see if there was any mail for us. Glad I went by myself – the young girl who opened the door said there'd been loads of phone calls and asked me if I was in some sort of trouble? I walked away with a stack of letters, all of them demands on overdue accounts. With great satisfaction and a sense of giddy liberation, I binned the lot of them in the middle of the busy high street.

**Monday 2 October, 2006**

**10.06 a.m. Office.** Text message received: 'MONEY ALERT – Please call CSL immediately quoting reference 123456'.

Just had a bit of a nasty surprise. Seems the credit chasers' reach has extended to my inbox.

**10.15 a.m.** Hm, thinking about the text message. Sounds like my debt's been passed on to a proper collections agency. If it has, then it could spell trouble, bringing on a new set of problems. Really don't fancy waking up to 'Meathead & Crowbar Associates' hammering down my door at dawn. Might crawl out of my foxhole to call the number and see where we're at.

**1.30 p.m. Office.** Walked across to the train station to use the public call box, which made me feel a bit like a secret agent. I dialled the number.

**Money-Chaser:** Good afternoon, Credit Solutions Limited, Money-grubber speaking, please can I take your reference number?

**Agent Livingson:** ——

**Money-Chaser:** Thanks, can I take your name?

**Agent Livingson:** Yes certainly it's Mr Cash.

**Money-Chaser:** Err Mr Cash? Can I take the reference again?

**Agent Livingson:** Yes of course, it's ——

**Money-Chaser:** I'm sorry Mr Cash, there seems to be some mistake. Sorry to bother you.

**Agent Livingson:** No trouble. If it was someone else you were looking for, I took this phone contract over from a friend.

**Money-Chaser:** Ah, who would that be?

**Agent Livingson:** Mr Livingson, he's living in Paris now.

**Money-Chaser:** He's living in Paris? How long has he been there for?

**Agent Livingson:** About two months.

**Money-Chaser:** Oh really, do you know when he's returning?

**Agent Livingson:** Oh, I think he's moved there indefinitely.

**Money-Chaser:** Well, if you happen to be in touch with him, can you ask him to call us with his reference number?

**Agent Livingson:** I'll see if I can get hold of him, can I ask what this is about?

**Money-Chaser:** I'm sorry sir, but under the Data Protection Act I'm not allowed to give out that information. He does need to call us though, it's not critical yet, but we do need to hear from him.

**Agent Livingson:** No problem, goodbye.


Hadn't planned to spin them a yarn, but when I began the call, the words just tumbled out. I shouldn't be enjoying this, but I am. Despite being at my desk, part of me feels like I might be in a Parisian café, drinking coffee and smoking rolled cigarettes, having left my worries behind. I don't care if they believe me or not. Just need to hold them off for a few more weeks.


**8.30 p.m. Home.** This game of cat and mouse is all well and good so long as it remains limited to a few calls and messages. Have to hold my nerve and stick to the plan – strike before it goes any further. Kelly's fears aside, in terms of my own worldly goods, they're more than welcome to them. It's absurd to remain in the debt trap for the sake of a few consumables. After all, the more you possess, the more you are possessed.


**Monday 9 October, 2006**

**11.56 a.m. Office.** Text message received: 'MONEY ALERT – Please contact Dan at CSL on —— quoting reference 123456.'

After a week of radio silence, they're trying to smoke me out. Perhaps their French connection is done scouring Parisian cafés and reported back to credit-chasing HQ?

**Tuesday 10 October 2006**
**3.30 p.m. Office.** It seemed rather pointless, but I went along with it anyway. I'm leaving in two days, but they still had me attend a three-hour 'inter-departmental' meeting as there was no one else to do it.

Sizing up the attendees as I took my seat, I was struck by the proportion of young ambitious-looking zealots mixed-in with the older heads. I noted during the round of introductions that these men who were my age, or perhaps younger, were already in management positions. I considered this as I sat there listening to the waffle. Having set out and established their goals, they had no doubt reached their intended career milestones ahead of schedule. They had followed the path and were making good progress and their satisfaction was evident in their smart but predictable attire, in their assertive confident mannerisms and enthusiastic talk.

As the meeting dragged on, with the young pups jostling for the spotlight, each talking at length to demonstrate their level of dedication and in-depth knowledge, I thought about what was required to reach their position. Total dedication, I concluded, as I listened to the inexorable blather filling the room. Absolute unadulterated devotion, involving hours and evenings spent reading dreary policy documents and dry legislation, but worst of all – actually having to care about it.

I looked over at one of the young men, observing the comically intent look on his face as he followed the discussion with an expression of genuine interest. I'd gathered from the pre-commencement chatter, that this fresh-faced, freckly chap with tight curly hair and a smooth dull face, had just returned from paternity leave after the birth of his first child. This was it for him, for all of them. Their futures were fixed. Being around them suddenly began to depress me and I began to get extremely fidgety. I looked at the clock. There was another half hour left. I stood up and walked out as if to visit the bathroom and left them all behind.

**Friday 13 October, 2006**
**2.00 p.m. Office.** Just a couple of hours to go. After months of dickless indecisiveness, I can feel my balls again. I've wrested back control of my life and changed its course.

**3.50 p.m.** I'm out of here in ten minutes. I'll sign the final timesheet and from then on I write my own rulebook. I'm still destined for the good life. I can feel it.

# Money Alert

*'If we've got a rise in indebtedness, if we've got a rise in people having difficulty servicing that debt… then maybe the banks are lending too much money, or maybe they're not being as careful as they used to be in scrutinising the applications. If they'd not lent it (the money) in the first place then they wouldn't be in the difficulty of trying to recover it.'*

Jim Fitzpatrick,
Trade and Industry Minister, 2006

Tuesday 17 October, 2006

**11.45 a.m. Home.** Goodbye to the whippersnapper years. Wrapped up in bed this morning after Kelly had left for work, happily juggling my balls as I pondered the day ahead.

**3.30 p.m.** The old man called to see how I was doing. I was in such great spirits I told him I'd quit my job.

'You didn't tell me you were thinking of moving on?' he said, taken aback at my sudden news.

'That's because I'm not moving,' I said correcting him. 'Think of it as a career break.'

'What d'ya mean a *career break*? Sitting on your arse won't pay the bills or your debts!' he shouted, predictably struggling to grasp the concept.

'Don't worry yourself,' I said rolling my eyes. 'I've made sure I've enough to see me through.'

'I can't believe you've left your old job without having anything else lined up. You better know what you're doing.'

'Oh, I know what I'm doing,' I assured him, catching sight of myself in the mirror and smiling at my reflection. 'I decided I needed some time out to reassess my life, to work out what I want to do with myself.' I ignored the waves of panic flooding down the phone line.

'But you've got a perfectly good career! You're not telling me you're gonna throw away all that study and all that experience. What on earth will you do?'

'I don't know yet, that's why I need time to think.'

'Well I've never heard anything like it,' he said in a fit of incredulity. 'I can't stay chatting all day, I have to go and lay some tarmac, some of us have to earn a crust.'

Wednesday 18 October, 2006

**2.30 p.m. Home.** Feel like I'm really getting a handle on this debt business. Listened to a fascinating interview on Radio 4 about the murky world of global finance and consumer debt. It may seem unbelievable, but the agreement you thought you signed with your lender, and the debt you're slavishly working to pay off, is being traded, sold, bought and played with on the world markets. So if the banks are no longer accountable, why on earth should you be? Surely we can do the same and sell our liability to the mad bloke at the street corner? Imagine using that as an excuse for non-payment. If the banks take this attitude towards us and our debts, surely it would be foolish not to reciprocate. Whose debt is it anyway?

### Thursday 19 October, 2006
**11.30 a.m. Home.** Great start to the day. News that losses are mounting at EGG: £39 million in the first half of this year and a similar amount predicted for the second half. The situation's being blamed on unexpected levels of default. I do hope they've factored me in.

### Monday 23 October, 2006
**11.45 a.m. Home.** Ah, this is the life. Only a week into my bankruptcy holiday and I already feel like I'm getting back in touch with myself. Spending most of my time buried in books and even writing a few lines of my own. Also doing a lot of walking and thinking, often wandering for miles without direction or purpose. On that note, it's time to get my coat – there are leaves to be crunched and twigs to be trampled upon!

**5.15 p.m.** Text message received: 'MONEY ALERT – Message from MBNA Europe, please call to discuss a query.' The one sour note to an otherwise glorious day.

### Thursday 26 October, 2006
**11.56 a.m. Home.** Text message received: 'MONEY ALERT – Please call CSL quoting reference —— '. Tedious.

### Monday 30 October, 2006
**2.54 p.m. Home.** Text message received: 'MONEY ALERT – Mr P. J. Livingson, please call QRI on —— '.

I'll be glad when this is over, it's getting to the point where I'm contemplating changing my number. Mint haven't been paid in a while, so they've joined in the chase.

### Thursday 2 November, 2006
**3.45 p.m. Home.** First roll of notes tucked safely under the mattress. The process of emptying my bank account has begun. It's yet another step towards liberation, I'm opting out of the banking system and reverting to a cash economy.

### Tuesday 7 November, 2006
**12.30 p.m. Home.** Account emptied. There's enough to pay this month's rent and the Court fee. Loan payments are due next week. With no money available, they'll simply bounce, putting me in arrears, paving the way for my day in court. After that, Kelly's kindly agreed to cover the rent until I'm earning again.

### Wednesday 8 November, 2006
**9.30 p.m. Home.** Almost shat myself when I opened the curtains this morning. Two big bruisers with shaved heads were getting out of a white van parked in front of the flat. I froze when they stopped and looked right at me before starting for my building. When I heard them ring the bell next door, I crept

quietly into the hall to press my ear up against the door. I sighed with relief, laughing at my own paranoia, when I realised they were removal men.

**Friday 10 November, 2006**
**11.00 a.m. Home.** Letter from EGG informing me that payment was missed and requesting I reinstate the direct debit that I've cancelled (forms enclosed for my convenience).

**1.50 p.m.** Phone's been ringing like an X Factor voting line. Got them all on my tail now.

**Thursday 16 November, 2006**
**2.25 p.m. Home.** Took a call purely out of curiosity. It was Virgin, offering me the mouth-watering incentive of a £15 credit on my account if I cleared all the arrears. I was even presented the 'opportunity' of this deal being extended until the end of the month. 'That sounds fantastic,' I said, mocking their pathetic token. Got rid of them with another hollow promise to pay.

**Saturday 18 November, 2006**
**4.30 p.m. Home.** In the run-up to bankruptcy, the daily perusal of debt forums has become something of an essential ritual. As well as providing detailed practical information on each stage of the process, they also serve as a barometer for the nation that's £1 trillion in the red.

The topic pages are full of cries for help from anxious borrowers; posts typically titled, 'SICK WITH IT ALL', 'I'M SO SCARED', 'I FEEL SO TRAPPED', 'FALLING APART', or 'ABOUT TO TAKE THE PLUNGE'. These forums are the

Skid Row of cyberspace; a virtual world of down-and-out debtors who can't even afford a packet of nuts in the 'last chance' saloon.

Realised I've been quite lucky after reading some of the stories. One guy said he'd been called a 'conman' and was threatened that his name 'would be splashed all over the newspapers' if he didn't pay up. Harmless threats with little basis in reality. Sure, your bankruptcy is advertised in the newspaper, but it's not exactly printed on the front page of *The Times* next to your mug shot. Just a few lines in some crummy local rag tucked away in the section nobody reads. But debt collection's a murky business. And in its dirty waters do float a few corpses: tragic cases of debt suicide, people unable to cope with the pressure, the harassment and the intimidation.

# Living the Dream

*'Personal bankruptcy may stigmatise or it may liberate, and these consequences may be different for different persons.'*

P. Shuchman,
An Attempt at a "Philosophy of Bankruptcy", 1973

**Monday 20 November, 2006**

**10.30 a.m. Home.** Only a month since I dropped out and I already feel like a new man.

Lying in bed this morning with my book and coffee, I looked over at the clock and thought about my former colleagues arriving at their desks to begin a new week. Letting out a hoot of delight, I burrowed myself under the covers, insulated by the warm cocoon of the flat, whilst outside, the cold city streets thronged with rushing hordes.

I'm living the dream, I reflected gleefully, as I put on my dressing gown and stood to look out of the window. Outside it was dark and raining, and the last of the yellowing leaves swirled in the wind. I leant against the frame, and breathed on the glass. Already, the thousands of days under strip lights seemed very far away, as if they had been a dream that never happened at all.

**Thursday 23 November, 2006**

**11.15 a.m. Text message received:** EGG: 'Please log into your account where an important message is waiting for you.'

Partly curious, or perhaps just suckered in by the 'important message', I logged in as instructed. The last thing I'd expected was to be met with a paternal arm around the shoulder, a welcome note assuring me that 'we could talk' if I was having trouble meeting the monthly payments. That something could be arranged: '*You don't have to worry on your own,*' it said.

Next to this disturbingly cosy greeting was a supposed quote from a satisfied customer, who'd apparently benefited from EGG's 'spread the love' approach. Could it be that the predatory lenders have been replaced by benevolent bankers?

More likely, they've been feeling the pinch from people defaulting, and they're desperate for people to keep paying. A more honest message would've read something like this: *'Dear Customer, please, please whatever you do, don't go bankrupt or default, as our profit margins are being wiped out by these instruments of freedom. You see, we're in a bit of pickle as we perhaps rather wishfully promised the City we'd make a profit in the second half of the year. We'll level with you, we really need your money. If you pick up the phone, it'll give us an opportunity to try and convince you to pay something, anything… Anything is better than nothing, right? Friend?'*

Break out the violins for the boys at EGG.

**11.30 a.m.** Telephoned the courthouse to fix an appointment for filing my bankruptcy petition. Got through on the second attempt, to be talked through the procedure by a very friendly court official. The lady told me to 'turn up on any weekday morning between the hours of 10 and 11' to join what I was warned was a 'long queue'.

She also advised me, I'd need to set aside the whole day as I'd have to visit the Official Receiver's office in the afternoon to hand in my bankruptcy petition, once it had been processed at the court. I had no idea it would take so long… Neh well, one solitary day to wipe out years of debt obligation is hardly something to weep about.

**12.00 p.m.** London's bankrupts have it tough. Whilst the rest of the country's debtors get away with a trip to some anonymous little county court, the capital's debtors are faced with a visit to no less than the *Royal Courts of Justice* on the Strand. Yep, that big intimidating courthouse that's always on the news. Still, there's a touch of poetic justice to it. As a destination on the Monopoly board, the Strand is a perfect venue to wash my hands of all that toy money.

**2.30 p.m.** Downloaded all the requisite papers and guidance notes from the Insolvency Service website: the official 'Bankruptcy Petition' and the daunting, 30-page 'Statement of Affairs'. An arduous form-filling exercise which must be completed before I can attend court. Plan to do the deed on Monday.

**9.30 p.m.** Damn it! I've missed a real trick. Reading through the guidance notes, there's a reminder about how you can't discharge student loan debts through bankruptcy. They quickly closed that loophole after a bunch of canny students realised how going bankrupt immediately after graduating would give them the best start in life. But it's only just hit me: what I should've done was use those bloody credit card cheques a few months ago to pay off my student loans. Well and truly kicking myself.

### Wednesday 29 November, 2006
**1.30 p.m. Home.** Having freed up some space in my wardrobe, I popped down to the print shop after breakfast in preparation for my crowning glory next week. I'm now the proud owner of a bespoke T-shirt, emblazoned with the slogan, 'BANKRUPT & LOVIN' IT'. The Turkish guy who runs the shop couldn't fathom it: 'How love bankruptcy? Bankruptcy bad'. At least he gave me a discount.

**3.33 p.m.** Spoke with MINT today. The little pup lovingly informed me that once an account was more than two months in arrears, it reflected badly on your credit file. Told him I'd do anything to protect my credit rating, before feeding him more cock 'n' bull about waiting to be paid in my fictitious new job. The next time his department hear from me will be via the Official Receiver.

**Thursday 30 November, 2006**
**1.45 p.m. Home.** Met up with Big Dave last night to tell him of my impending insolvency. As expected, I was spared an outpouring of moral outrage from my fellow card carrier:

'Are you for real?' he asked, not quite sure how to react, and looking at me quizzically.

'Of course,' I replied, before briefly explaining my reasons. 'I'm not prepared to wait for my freedom. I've already quit my job.'

He was speechless and didn't know whether to commiserate or congratulate. I spared him the dilemma.

'Are you coming to my bankruptcy bash?' I asked. 'I'm having a big party next week to celebrate.'

His serious face changed into a smile, 'You're having a fucking party? You funny fucker.'

'Too right, I'm taking a picnic blanket and a hamper crammed full of champers into the foyer of HSBC. The challenge is to drain all the bottles by the time the police arrive to chuck us out or arrest us.'

'You're winding me up you twat,' he said clamping his hands to his temples in amused disbelief.

'Why not?' I said, managing to hold a straight face. 'Actually I was wondering whether you'd mind standing by the door and handing out copies of my *Mass Default Manifesto*.'

'Your mass what?'

'Massive wind-up,' I said, rocking back in my chair and slapping my leg.

'You're off your bloody rocker,' said Dave, shaking his head and chuckling into his pint glass.

Without thinking, and perhaps for selfish reasons – Dave was the one person I knew who was in deeper shit than me and we always derive comfort from knowing someone's worse off than we are – I spoilt the good mood by asking him about his level of debt.

He let out a heavy sigh before answering sheepishly: '70 fucking grand mate.'

I didn't blink, I'd expected as much.

'It wasn't just the holidays either,' his tone had shifted to sound confessional.

'Tell ya the truth, about half of that went up my nose,' he said regretfully.

'Ain't touched it for months but, well, I've been a fuckin' idiot and now I'm fucked.'

At that point he looked really low. I knew he was partial to just a few lines, not exactly the next *Scarface*.

'You're definitely off it?'

'Fuck yeah, 100%, learnt my lesson there. Look, you're the only person I've told about this, so keep it tuh y'self right. The 70 grand's bad enuf but the other thing…'

'I won't tell a soul,' I said.

He looked miserable.

'It's costing me about £800 a month just to pay the minimum. I have to take out more money at the end of the month and the debt keeps getting bigger.'

'You have to go bankrupt,' I implored. I couldn't see any other way out for him.

'No way, I ain't doin' that. I'll be fucked for years.'

'And you're not now?'

'Yeah but fucked in every way. I'll never be able to get a mortgage. Jesus, we're pushing 30, we should be securing our future, not bloody bankrupting ourselves. If my parents found out, they'd disown me.'

'So what then?'

'Well, I've started working overtime and I'm due some big commissions. And I'm buying a flat with my brother, hopefully that'll help pay it off.'

Hearing his 'solution' depressed me greatly. I quickly realised there was little point in trying to force my opinions on him: a man always has to reach his own conclusions. Also had to check myself from asking about his plans to emigrate, it was clear he wasn't going anywhere for a long time.

The waiter arrived with another round of drinks.

'I'll get this mate,' offered Dave.

'Don't be stupid, put your money away,' I said, even though he was brandishing a MasterCard.

'In a couple of days, I won't have any debt, so it's my shout.'

But Dave was insistent.

'No seriously, let me. After all, what's another few quid when you owe 70 grand?' We looked at each other and began laughing into our beer. We spent the rest of the night getting drunk and talking about our accelerated lifestyles, all the fun we'd had over the last few years, living like miniature kings on plastic thrones.

### Friday 1 December, 2006

**2.30 p.m. Home**. Managed to complete the paperwork, and I'm good to go for Monday's showdown with the judge. Listing my assets was a breeze: basically marked 'NONE' in each of the columns. Recording all my debts in the 'unsecured creditors' section was also extremely satisfying. This should be the last time I'm ever confronted with those figures.

Not all of it was quite so straightforward. Spotted something of a landmine buried in Section 8 of the Debtor's Petition: '*The Official Receiver may need to tell your landlord that you are bankrupt.*'

Something I wasn't previously aware of. Strikes me as rather unnecessary if there are no rent arrears. Just have to cross my fingers on that one.

The possibility for a really nasty surprise lay in Section 7 of the Statement of Affairs, where you're required to list your outgoings in order for the Official Receiver to establish your full financial details. The accompanying guidance notes state, '*It may be possible that following payment for all your outgoings each month, you will be able to make a contribution to your creditors.*'

Talk about 'minding the small print'. Luckily I'd already encountered this in the course of my preparations. It's a potentially lethal tripwire, but with a little foresight, it's a snare that can easily be sidestepped.

Following your bankruptcy, if there's enough money left in your disposable income once essential living expenses have been deducted, something known as an Income Payments Order (IPO) is made against you, that forces you to make a contribution to the cost of your bankruptcy and to your creditors. This is usually 50% of your disposable income, payable for up to three years.

But what's the point of putting yourself through bankruptcy, only to find yourself still paying three years later? There's a clear solution to avoiding this, and that's to make damn sure there isn't any disposable income for them to claim. *Play the system*, get a job that just covers the basics, live frugally for the length of your bankruptcy and you'll be cut free without having to pay another penny. Plus, a requirement to earn very little, means working very little. So it's win-win for the wily debtor. And therein lies the rub: by design, the bankruptcy rules encourage a period of hardship and simplicity – a perfect antidote to the spiritually damaging effects of consumerism and the cult of work. I'm almost tempted to think some sort of visionary was the architect of the present-day insolvency laws, but that would be stretching it.

The IPO was introduced to address criticism of the process from creditors: that bankrupts were enjoying good lifestyles while their debts remained unpaid. But enjoying a good lifestyle isn't necessarily synonymous with earning a fat income. With an incentive to stay at home rather than go out to make money that would only go towards your creditors, you are basically encouraged to embrace the part-time lifestyle for the duration of your bankruptcy. After all, time is our most precious commodity. How often does one hear an entrenched worker wistfully express the desire for a 'time-out'? A much-needed breathing space to reconnect with themselves and reassess their life? Indeed. The opportunity to stretch the bankrupt's holiday is not to be sniffed at.

**9.30 p.m.** I wasn't entirely joking when I told Big Dave I was having a post-bankruptcy celebration. Come Monday morning, I'll be heading straight from the courthouse to the public house.

I'm not talking about just any old boozer, I'm targeting the Daniel Defoe of Hackney. Defoe is surely the patron saint of bankruptcy, having managed this feat not once, but twice in his lifetime.

Ah yes, the sweet taste of freedom will soon be mine.

# 1970 Was a Good Year

*'In the short-term, which is what politicians live for, it is a
sound policy to keep people borrowing and spending at about the
present rate, in order to sustain economic growth. The thousands of
people driven to bankruptcy will just blame themselves, so it's win-
win for the government.'*

Nick Faulkner, Are We Deliberately Driven to Bankruptcy?
2006

### Sunday 3 December, 2006

**11.15 p.m. Home.** 'Tis the night before bankruptcy. Thoughts are only of tomorrow, will there really be a long snaking queue of people? How will I be treated? What will it feel like at the decisive moment when I'm standing before the judge, hearing the sound of the hammer immediately followed by those magic words: 'Paul Joseph Livingson, I officially declare you bankrupt'.

One thing's for sure, in less than twenty four hours I'll be on the other side of the door and the world of debt will be behind me.

**11.35 p.m.** Hic! Been getting stuck into the wine to ensure a decent night's kip.

**12.05 a.m.** 'I'm going bankrupt in the morning, ding dong! the bells are gonna chime....' Kelly's telling me to ease up and save the celebrations for tomorrow.

### Monday 4 December, 2006

**8.15 a.m. Home.** Up and at 'em – it's the big day. First port of call is the Fees Office. Have to pay the entrance tax before the court will consider my Debtor's Petition. Packing my notebook as I'm anticipating a lot of hanging around.

**9.20 a.m. Courthouse.** Arrived at the Strand under a glorious sky, the Royal Courts of Justice buildings looking positively magnificent in the sunshine. I've rolled the dice, I thought to myself as I chained my bike to the railings, and I've landed on the right square, armed with my 'get out of jail free' card.

**9.25 a.m. Fees Office.** Sitting outside the Fees Office waiting for it to open. Unfashionably early, so it's fairly quiet. Had to negotiate airport-style security scanners at the entrance, before making my way through the cavernous Great Hall to get to here. It's the first thing you notice about this place: the scale of it; physically it's very intimidating. Although the fear factor was reduced somewhat when I spotted official souvenirs for sale by the entrance – *Whether it's murder, rape or bankruptcy, be sure to pick up a memento of your day in court by visiting our gift shop.* The pick of the bunch was 'Barrister Bear' weighing in at a hefty £18. Alas, I'll be leaving empty-handed. Even at a modest £6.75, a 'Royal Courts of Justice' Parker Pen is beyond my means.

**9.30 a.m.** Half an hour till the office opens. Goddamnit. Itching to get on with things. Am experiencing a touch of nervous anticipation, akin to being in the dressing room before a football match. Just me and another so far; a well-dressed ponytailed guy wearing designer jeans, tan shoes and an expensive sweater. He's probably here to see the fashion police, it's 2006 after all – nobody should be allowed to get away with wearing a ponytail *and* an earring. He's been rabbiting away like a stock broker, conducting business on his phone since I arrived.

**9.45 a.m.** Almost time for kick-off. Court staff have begun arriving for work, laughing and joking, bringing a sense of normality to the proceedings. There's also been a late surge, about 15 people hanging around the door of the office. Probably a deliberate tactic for avoiding uncomfortable small talk.

**10.15 a.m. Toilets.** That was fairly painless, in and out in five minutes. Rather ironically, with its counter and cashiers, the Fees Office is laid out exactly like a bank. I kept this witty observation to myself, as the impeccably polite teller processed my payment, stamped my Debtor's Petition and handed me my receipt. Afterwards, I paid a brief visit to another room a couple of doors down to present my papers and receive instructions on the next phase. As I prepare to move on, people are still arriving. Looks like it's a busy day.

**10.25 a.m. Thomas More Building – Bankruptcy Room.** Had to find my way across the complex to reach the bankruptcy 'court'. Took the lift up to the 1st floor and now am standing in a queue waiting to have my Debtor's Petition examined. I must look like a journalist or a poorly disguised mystery shopper, standing here scribbling away in my notebook. Louis Theroux's got nothing on me.

**10.35 a.m.** No movement yet, the staff aren't ready for us. Getting the feeling that much of the day will be spent like this: standing around waiting for things to happen. Almost forgot to turn my phone off. It'd be just like my old man to call while I'm here.

**10.50 a.m.** At last, we're underway. A girl up ahead has moved to the counter, and I can hear her swearing her Statement of Affairs on oath.

**10.55 a.m.** Important note: one half of the bankruptcy room is set aside for individual insolvencies and the other for companies. But it's this side that's heaving with people whilst the 'companies' area remains completely deserted. Empirical evidence that it's the people who've taken advantage of recent insolvency reforms that were introduced to encourage more enterprise.

**11.00 a.m.** Well, it's not something you do everyday: standing in a line of aspiring bankrupts. Been casting discreet glances down the room at the people here. Nobody's making eye contact, and there's an atmosphere of everybody just wanting to get it over with. Only two Asian girls in front of me seem in good spirits. I get the feeling one of them is here for moral support and is acting as 'bankruptcy coach' for the other. From the sound of her advice, she's certainly very knowledgeable on the subject.

A middle-aged pair standing a few places back seem particularly agitated, looking around the room, muttering to each other in sharp, hushed voices. They look like simple folk and remind me of those broken couples who feature in Ocean Finance adverts on daytime TV. I can easily picture them in a commercial, perched nervously on a worn sofa, close to tears as they espouse the virtues of a consolidation loan. Ocean Finance – repackaging misery since 1991.

**11.05 a.m.** A fair proportion of today's roll call appear to be from the lower end of the social spectrum, which debt historians will tell you is indicative of a shift in the nature of borrowing, as traditionally the working classes have always been averse to debt, out of fear of not being able to pay it back. But times have changed.

**11.10 a.m.** I can't help but be surprised by the age groups in this congregation either. They span the generations: from young 20-somethings to middle-aged people and, unbelievably, even a couple of pensioners. For me, in the prime of life and here to tell the banks to go fuck themselves, this is a cakewalk, but to see old folk standing here is extremely sad. Britain 2006 – where you see pensioners in the bankruptcy court. Brutal Britain, where people in their autumn years are chased for council tax arrears and energy bills. Barbaric.

**11.20 a.m.** Won't be long before it's my turn. The queue remains about 20-strong, as people do their stuff and trickle out through the doors.

**11.25 a.m.** A smart young blonde at the back of the line just caught my attention, looking away sheepishly as our eyes met. *Nothing to be ashamed of love, we're all here for the same thing.* If there's one place to purge yourself of any status anxieties, it's being in a line of insolvent debtors at the bankruptcy court – the Lourdes of Consumerism. By the look of her chic clothes, I'm guessing her attendance is the result of one shopping binge too many.

Queue moving up. I'm next.

**12.10 p.m. Bar Italia, Soho.** Out on good behaviour – time for a spot of lunch whilst they process my Debtor's Petition. It didn't take long for the court administrator – another commendably affable and courteous member of staff – to check through my forms. Being an Atheist, I had to swear 'affirmation without book'. Having had my documents verified, I was instructed to return at 2:30 p.m. to discover whether my petition's been accepted.

Huge shock when I enquired when we'd be going before the judge. Was dismayed to learn that this part of the process has been done away with. So I won't get to hear the sound of the hammer after all. I haven't felt this disappointed since I visited Buckingham Palace as a boy and came away without having tea with the queen.

**12.20 p.m.** One person every minute – count me in. All morning, similar scenes have been played out in County Courts across the land, the annual insolvency tally increasing steadily as it climbs to an unprecedented level. From millstone to milestone for 100,000 debtors – bliss.

**2.45 p.m. Room 110, Thomas More Building.** In the antechamber of insolvency, awaiting word that I've made the cut. We're all crammed into a miserable little space, resembling a doctor's waiting room. The flickering strip lights are giving me a headache and the faded blue walls make me feel sick. It's very busy too, everyone's here, the entire cast of London's latest bankrupt. 'London's Latest Bankrupt' – sounds like the title of a reality show. If only I knew somebody at Channel 4.

The seats in here are arranged so that everyone faces everyone else. I've ended up next to Ponytail again. He's thumbing his way through the second-hand car section of *LOOT* as he plans for life after his Mercedes-Benz. The Ocean Finance couple, looking as tragic as ever, are like two statues, staring straight ahead in stony silence.

Everyone's waiting for their name to be called and to be handed back their papers. Then it'll be a dash for the finish line – a hop, skip and jump to the Official Receiver's Office, around the corner in Bloomsbury. Any minute now, I'll find out whether I'm officially 'a bankrupt'.

**3.05 p.m.** Here we go, drum roll please: names are being called…

**3.25 p.m. Official Receiver's Office, Insolvency Service HQ, Bloomsbury.** Sitting in the lobby at Insolvency HQ, having entered the final phase. Pedal power ensured I was first here. Already registered at reception and now waiting for a member of staff to come and get me for the interview. After that I'm free to go. Good job too – I'm spitting feathers. I've definitely earned a pint.

**3.30 p.m.** This place is a far cry from the dreary confines of the court: it's all potted plants and glass doors. Very corporate. It's surprisingly tranquil in here, the kind of hushed stillness and order one would find in a company reception area. More importantly, I am now in possession of the magic slip, the one I've been waiting for – I'm officially bankrupt.

**5.40 p.m. The Daniel Defoe Public House.** Walked into the pub and ordered myself a pint of Tribute (a fittingly named Cornish ale). Was almost dancing on the spot and unable to suppress a grin as the barmaid handed me my prize. With trembling hands I lifted the glass to my lips and very quietly, in the manner of a religious rite, uttered the words, 'To Daniel Defoe and bankruptcy', before the sweet golden liquid slipped down my throat.

**5.50 p.m.** Kelly's on her way down to join me before the real party begins. The interview in Bloomsbury was unexpectedly brief and incredibly good-natured. A young man greeted me in the reception area and cordially informed me that he'd been assigned to my case, then collected a visitor's pass on my behalf and escorted me to a small room. The insolvency practitioner proceeded to read my forms, asking me several questions about the information on my petition, including how and when I'd acquired my debts. The consultation lasted about fifteen minutes, after which I was informed that I'd be automatically discharged exactly one year from now, maybe even sooner, since my case appeared so straightforward. Then he told me to pass on my bankruptcy reference number to my creditors who would now have to leave me alone. Adieu my little credit puppets!

**6.00 p.m.** Collected my second pint from the bar, whereupon I lit a cigarette before raising my glass to Defoe again, this time to his second bankruptcy. My friends will be arriving soon, to join me for my coronation as Crown Prince of Bankruptcy.

# Twilight of the Bank Managers

*'This isn't just a problem for the people caught up in rising debts. It's a potential problem for everyone. An economy built on borrowed money is an economy built on borrowed time.'*

*George Osborne, Shadow Chancellor, 2006*

Tuesday 5<sup>th</sup> December, 2006

**10.45 a.m. Bed.** Big bankruptcy bender. Lost count of the amount of times glasses were raised to my freedom from debt. Felt like a bank robber celebrating a heist with his cronies.

**11.05 a.m. Mirror.** The moment of truth: time to face my own reflection.

**11.07 a.m.** All is well. Contrary to popular perception, I'm displaying no signs of physical mutation and have absolutely not been turned into an insect or a leper. I am still a man with his whole life ahead of him.

**11.10 a.m.** Slipped into my 'Bankrupt & Loving It' T-shirt. Took a snap on my mobile and messaged it to a select few.

**11.20 a.m.** Jez called from Bristol in a state of disbelief. 'Explain!' he said excitedly. 'Have you *really* gone bankrupt?'

I told him I had. 'And… no more working for the man!' I boasted. He pissed himself laughing. 'Yeah, tell the banks to go fuck themselves,' he spluttered. He sounded like he was crying. 'You fucking chief!'

**11.30 a.m.** No doubt this'll take a while to sink in, but I keep telling myself, yesterday you had thousands of pounds of debt to your name and today you have none. The feeling's comparable to that of a birthday: you wake up a year older but no great metamorphosis has occurred.

It's a shame they don't make bankruptcy-themed greeting cards, then it would really feel like a birthday. I'd have bolted out of bed this morning to collect the post and sat opening all the cards from friends and family congratulating me on my insolvency status. No doubt some of them would've done the decent thing and slipped a tenner inside to buy me a celebratory drink. Christ, maybe I could put together a few prototypes before pitching it to Hallmark. I can picture my designs on the shelves: 'Happy Bankruptcy' cards complete with a 'Bankrupt Today' lapel badge. It'd be a real gas dreaming up messages to put inside them…

> *Think of all your wishes,*
> *And all the things you'd like to do,*
> *Happy bloody bankruptcy,*
> *It's a debt-free life for you*

*Dear Paul,*
*Congratulations on your bankruptcy, enjoy your special day.*
*All our love, Aunty Maude and Uncle Peter x x x*

**6.30 p.m.** That's my Bankruptcy Order framed and up on the wall in the lounge, occupying pride of place next to my other notable achievement, the certificate awarded to me in 1987 for swimming 400 metres breaststroke (without stopping).

### Wednesday 6 December, 2006
**10.30 a.m. Home.** Here we go. Two letters in the post, one from HSBC, the other from Mint. HSBC have written to inform me they've deducted my personal loan instalment from my current account and plan to charge me £25 for being over my limit. The several million pennies have yet to drop and they're still rubbing their hands with glee in the belief they'll be profiting from the situation.

The tone of the letter from Mint is much more urgent and serious: *Why has the overdue amount on your account not been paid? We have brought this matter to your attention previously and advised you of the consequences of non-payment. We hoped that you would respond to our request. Do you have any intention of repaying this debt?*

That last line is priceless.

**12.00 p.m.** More bad news for HSBC. Their share price has dropped as a result of bad debts in the UK and defaults in the US, affecting their mortgage business. They're crying foul over the laws in the UK that make it easy for people to escape their creditors. To quote their chief exec: 'There are people out there encouraging people to file for bankruptcy… It's something the industry and the government need to look at. Is this the right type of law for what it set out to achieve?'

Looks like I timed my move to perfection. It won't be long before they're lobbying for a tightening of the rules. And they'll no doubt succeed, given the government's habit of kowtowing to the demands of big business.

**Thursday 7 December, 2006**
**10.45 a.m. Home.** This country. A mere three days after being declared bankrupt and I'm already being targeted with mail-shots by a company trying to cash in on the situation. It beggars belief. They've even adopted an official sounding name, calling themselves, 'The Insolvency Advisory Service':

*Dear Mr Livingson,*

*Is this you? Been made bankrupt? Just when you thought it could not get any worse you now have a Trustee trying to claim everything you have ever owned AND MORE!*
*We believe we are the best – we only work for you, not your creditors. Generally, we have more knowledge than most Trustees. One phone call and a free meeting will demonstrate ...'*

Another day, another letter in the bin.

**Monday 11 December, 2006**
**3.45 p.m. Home.** EGG called. Broke the good news to them and now somebody in their office is busy tapping in the details, moving another few grand into the 'bad debt' column on the mother spreadsheet.

**Thursday 14 December, 2006**
**11.55 a.m. Home.** Spoke with MBNA yesterday and MINT today. I'm off their radar for good.

**Friday 22 December, 2006**
**12.30 p.m. Home.** About time I heard from them, my own bank – Bombay Branch.

'Good morning Mr Livingson,' said the caller, with a strong Indian accent. 'I'm calling to advise you that your current account is in arrears and that you have significantly exceeded your overdraft limit. I must also tell you that your personal loan is due for payment shortly and you have insufficient funds in your account to cover the payment. Can I ask when you intend to rectify the situation?'

'Never,' I said defiantly.

'I'm sorry sir,' said the woman, sounding confused as though she'd misheard.

'I'm never going to pay,' I bragged. 'I'm not giving you another penny.' This last statement was delivered triumphantly.

Of course, it was totally pointless and incredibly childish to be flaunting my default to somebody at the bottom of the big corporate pyramid like this, but I really couldn't help myself.

'Can I ask why?' enquired the lady, sounding totally lost. The computer script obviously didn't cover such an eventuality. Having expected to hear either a raft of excuses or a commitment to pay, I could sense she was desperately clicking buttons, scrambling for some kind of instruction.

'I'm not paying because I declared myself bankrupt a few days ago,' I answered. 'But while I'm on the line, can I ask just how much money I've escaped giving you?'

Amazingly, the poor woman began robotically reading out the outstanding totals on my accounts as if I'd phoned with a general enquiry.

I responded to the totals by asking rhetorically, 'Do you know how many years I would have had to work to pay that off?'

I caught hold of myself and left it there. It was futile and a bit mean. After all, it was hardly the CEO on the line. I gave her the details of my bankruptcy and she then informed me that I'd still receive letters. I pointed out that this was absurd, but it was their money and they could continue sending letters if they liked.

**3.30 p.m.** New Year's around the corner, a natural time for introspection and thinking about the future. 2006 was all about the bid for freedom. Next year will be about how best to use it.

**3.40 p.m.** Some men need work. For them, a job is everything: the foundation of their self-esteem, something to believe in, what gives their life purpose. Others devote themselves to the pursuit of wealth, prosperity, status and comfort. I have almost perished in the company of such creatures.

Now I have realised that, generally speaking, modern forms of employment are graveyards for the human spirit. Alongside the willing are millions of men who are slowly dying at work, because it takes them away from themselves. These same men, once freed from their duties and responsibilities and granted their time, are able to grow and draw closer to that which is so desirable, so admirable in man.

I have created the conditions for a life of my own choosing, for the only kind of growth that matters. Give me a bookshelf, a pen and a blank page. 2007 and beyond: discontent gives way to fulfilment.

# The People vs. The Banks

*'The issue which has swept down the centuries and which will have to be fought sooner or later is the people versus the banks.'*

Lord Acton, 19th century Historian

**Thursday 28 December, 2006**

**12.30 a.m. Milton Keynes.** The enormity of my recent actions was brought home to me as I shook the old man's hand when we arrived for Christmas dinner at his place. It was my first encounter with him since I became bankrupt.

He answered the door, already wearing a bright red crumpled paper hat, pulled from a Christmas cracker. He ushered us in warmly. His good mood, which eased my initial anxiety, was down to the fact that the new house was almost ready. He reckoned there were just a couple of months of tidying up before the grand unveiling.

'Are you having an opening ceremony?' I asked playfully, after we'd stuffed ourselves with turkey and trimmings.

'Why, I suppose so,' he replied warily.

'I'll write to Prince Charles, see if he can do the honours, only I think the Queen's diary's a little full this time of year.'

'Bah, y'cheeky sod.'

When we were done exchanging presents, he asked for a progress report on my debt repayment efforts.

'Oh they're all paid off now,' I said dismissively, being more than economical with the truth, and draining my wine glass.

Thankfully, Jan stepped in to preserve the good atmosphere: 'C'mon, we're having a nice time, let's not ruin it with that sort of talk.'

Later, Kelly bowed to Dad and Jan's request to sing a few numbers. It was a nice moment, they were chuffed that she sang for them and were genuinely impressed by her talent. Although Jan almost blew it by suggesting she audition for 'X Factor'. I had to tactfully explain the concept of 'integrity' and that this was the last thing she'd consider doing.

Tuesday 9 January, 2007

**10.30 a.m. Home.** Here's a friendly New Year missive – official confirmation from HSBC:

*Dear Mr Livingson,*

*Following receipt of a Bankruptcy Order, your accounts with HSBC have been frozen.*

*Please return your cards and any unused cheques to this office within the next seven days.*

*We are obliged to serve demand on you for the full amount of your indebtedness and this is attached. No further action is required by you in relation to this demand.*

Friday 12 January, 2007

**6.30 p.m. Home.** Had my worst fears confirmed when our landlady called earlier to say she'd received a letter about my bankruptcy. *Here we go*, I thought. *We're getting the boot.* I was already panicking about how on earth I was going to break this to Kelly, when I heard her say she had no issue with us, since we'd always paid the rent, and that provided we continued to do so, we could stay. She was actually rather sympathetic, assuming student debts to be the cause of my financial meltdown. I didn't bother to correct her.

**7.00 p.m.** Can't understand the Official Receiver's decision to write to the landlord: there were no rent arrears on my petition. A quick post on a debt forum confirmed this to be an unusual course of action on their part. Pah! Why waste energy on it, we're not being evicted and that's all that matters.

Tuesday 16 January, 2007

**11.15 a.m. Home.** Times are hard, relatively speaking. Spent the morning emptying the moneybox of coins to buy some groceries. Even resorted to digging behind the cushions of the sofas in a throwback to my student days, when we'd tear the house apart trying to cobble together funds for another bag of weed. After three months of blissful indolence, I have to get a job. Nothing too heavy of course, no more than a few hours a week to keep me under the radar.

Wednesday 24 January, 2007

**1.45 p.m. Home.** Landed a part-time gig at the university round the corner. Job's a breeze, the place is crawling with hot young women in desperate need of assistance, and everyday feels like Friday.

Friday 2 February, 2007

**4.20 p.m. Home.** Could it be that after more than a century of waiting, Lord Acton's prophecy of a showdown between the people and the banks is beginning to come true? Today's announcement from the Insolvency Service has confirmed that an unprecedented 107,288 people were declared insolvent last year.

In my optimistic moments, I envisage a rebellion on the scale of the Poll Tax riots, an embodiment of our 'can't pay, won't pay' attitude that rises to the surface when the dark forces push us too hard and make the lives of ordinary people impossible. Imagine tens of thousands of protestors pouring into the City of London and Canary Wharf, the scenes of disorder being beamed across the world. But when my thoughts turn gloomy and I'm at my most pessimistic, my faith in the people's propensity to revolt vanishes. Our society of comfort and wealth has cultivated a deep-rooted apathy where we only rise up… to change the TV channel.

**Sunday 4 February, 2007**
**5.00 p.m. Aftermath of a Battleground.** My neighbour Charlotte just popped down to check everyone was still alive. I sheepishly apologised for the commotion and assured her everything was fine, before retrieving Kelly from the café around the corner where she'd escaped to seek cover.

The old fella had driven down to drop off some spare furniture for us, as his palace is being decked out with new stuff from IKEA. I was in the kitchen happily making tea when I felt a strange presence behind me. I turned with a start to see the old man, standing a couple of feet away with a face like thunder, holding my framed Bankruptcy Order in his hand. I froze, rooted to the spot as he stood there glowering, silently shaking the frame at me.

I'd forgotten to take it down from the wall in the lounge, where he'd been sat chatting to Kelly. The glaring stand-off was broken by the sound of the front door closing as Kelly slipped out.

'Is this what I think it is?' he said in that hushed, no-nonsense tone I'd not heard since my youth.

I looked at him seething and quivering, holding my Bankruptcy Order like he was going to cave my skull in with it. I couldn't think of anything to say. He'd turned the frame around so that I was confronted with my bankruptcy. I thought about saying it was a joke gift from somebody, but I wasn't about to risk provoking him further, not when I could see that his hand trembled and shook. I had to look up and as our eyes met, it seemed to ignite something inside him. I jumped as he suddenly slammed the frame to the floor – the sharp sound of splintering glass filling the room. He turned without looking at me and walked off into the lounge.

I finished making the tea, stepped over the scattered shards and went to join him in the front room. I entered to see him standing at the window with his back to me. I set the mugs on the coffee table and after the longest couple of minutes in my life, he turned around to look at me as though I'd just told him I was a serial killer. He still couldn't bring himself to speak. He kept rubbing his face, sitting down and standing up, walking to the window, sitting down again. He was clearly shell-shocked and I worried I might've rendered him mute or worse still, might cause him to have a heart attack.

'Are you just gonna keep pacing about like that?' I said, desperate for him to say what he wanted.

He looked at me in disgust. 'My son a bankrupt,' he stammered, shaking his head in disbelief before sitting down and balancing on the edge of the chair, his body hunched forward.

'My son a bankrupt, I can't believe it.' He put his head in his hands. I thought he was going to cry.

I waited for him to speak again as another excruciating silence descended on the room.

'So this is what you meant about clearing your debts?' he said disgustedly. 'All this time you were lying to us, making out you'd paid it all off when, when…' he faltered, 'when you were behaving like a common crook.'

'Now hang on a minute,' I protested. 'That's a bit harsh. All right – I made a few mistakes, but I am no crook. You have no idea what it was like, being in that much debt.'

'But why didn't you come to me? I would've bloody lent you the money,' he cried, his voice rising to a dog-like howl.

'Because I'd still have to pay it back,' I said, realising I was leaving myself open.

'Of course you have to pay it back if you *borrow* it!' he bellowed, spitting with fury.

'But it was my responsibility and my problem,' I stressed again. 'I chose not to pay it for a very good reason.'

'Oh this'll be good, I'm all ears,' he boomed. I heard the scraping of a chair in the flat above, we were obviously disturbing the neighbours.

'Because,' I started, 'I didn't see why my life should be ruined by greedy fucking banks that throw money at people to make obscene profits. There's millions of people like me, millions out there, who've been tricked into becoming slaves of the banks. But I wouldn't expect you to see that,' I wheezed, getting out of breath. 'Yes, I did it because it was convenient. But I also did it as a matter of principle. I wanted to take a stand, I did it for me and for everyone who's ever been fucked over by the banks.'

'Principle!' he screamed, almost choking himself. 'That's the last thing you should be talking about, bloody *principles*. I've never heard anything so ridiculous in all my life. You can't go bankrupt just because it's convenient, no matter what!' he wailed, leaning forward in his chair pointing his finger at me. 'And you *certainly* can't do it because of some hare-brained ideals!'

I just wanted him out of the house. I'd never intended to tell him about my bankruptcy. A cooling-off period was needed. We could talk about it more rationally once he'd had a chance to come to terms with it. Unfortunately this wasn't going to happen.

'So that's why you've not been working. It all makes sense now,' he said, thinking aloud, piecing together the jigsaw. 'It's disgusting it's, it's…'

We were both breathing heavily. We were like two boxers pacing around the ring. My heart was pounding. I felt boiling hot and had to peel off my jumper.

'You know what son…' he said standing up and moving towards me with only the tiny coffee table separating us. 'You know what you are? You're *morally* bankrupt. That's right, *morally bankrupt*,' and he leaned into my face.

I refused to answer his charge and held my ground, standing with my arms folded across my chest.

'You shouldn't be allowed to get away with it,' he said climbing onto his pious perch. 'You know they used to throw people like you in jail.'

'Not anymore they don't,' I said unable to resist. I'd had enough of his bullshit. 'In fact, you'll no doubt be dismayed to learn that a law passed in 1970 abolished imprisonment for civil debt. And what's more, the 1970 law protects debtors from prison *regardless* of whether their default was deliberate or a mistake. I've not committed fraud, everything I've done was within the boundaries of the law.'

'Listen to you, you think you're so bloody smart don't you? Well let me tell you, you've ruined your life, you little idiot. You'll never get a mortgage now, and if you ever want to run a business, forget it. You see how easy things are for you now.'

He stepped back, his face trembling. I too was shaking.

'And that picture, putting it up on your wall like that,' he said looking at the empty space next to my swimming certificate. 'It's just one big joke to you isn't it?'

He'd really lost his rag. He grabbed his keys and made to leave, before turning suddenly in the doorway: 'Y'know if people knew I was a bankrupt, I'd never be able to hold my head up,' he said with his fierce eyes fixed on me. 'I wouldn't be able to look them in the eyes. Don't you feel any shame? Are you not the least bit ashamed?'

I stood rooted to the spot, offering no response. Not that he waited for it. No doubt concluding that this was a fitting way to leave, he turned and I watched him stomp down the street and get into his car. I felt mighty relieved when he'd gone. I sat there for half an hour to make sure he wasn't coming back, before going to fetch Kelly.

Kelly was more than a little rattled when I relayed the details of our blow-up. 'At least it's out in the open,' she offered by way of comfort.

**10.00 p.m.** Well, there's been no fatal car crashes on the news, so I'm assuming he got home safely.

### Thursday 8 February, 2007

**8.30 p.m. Home.** Called the old man's house to make sure he hadn't been admitted to hospital. Jan answered the phone: 'We're not speaking to you,' she said coldly. 'Your father's inconsolable.'

Talk about melodrama. I refused to pander to their cold-shouldering, and hung up with a resigned, 'Fine then, have it your way'. I'll leave them to stew on it, they'll come round eventually.

### Friday 9 February, 2007

**10.30 a.m. Home.** Slept badly last night. But the deed was done and there was no turning back. Still, it took me hours of tossing and turning to dig down and find my resolution again. In your own circles, surrounded by like-minded people, your ideas seem strong and sound. It's easy to forget that the rest of the world thinks differently.

As I got up to smoke a cigarette to escape the oppressive blackness of the bedroom, I sat thinking about his final words. I felt no shame, none of the dishonour he associated with it. It was different for me. I hadn't the pressure of a family who I felt that I had somehow let down, there was no primal guilt of having failed to provide. Neither did I have to concern myself with becoming the town pariah. I had no business associates to face, there was no desperate dependency on the charity or goodwill of others.

I was sorry for my father, sorry that he'd found out and had to deal with it. But I was still glad I did it. I had saved myself. I could see that more clearly than ever. Not only had I saved myself, my actions had enabled me to start a new life. Free from a debt-strapped existence, I was back in command of my own future – and that mattered more than anything.

**Tuesday 20 February, 2007**

**10.15 a.m. Home.** Today's papers are full of reports of the banks having been forced to write off a record £6.6 billion of bad debt for last year as a result of mass default: Barclays £1.67 billion, Lloyds TSB £1.26 billion, HBOS £1.24 billion, Royal Bank of Scotland £1.34 billion, and bringing up the rear, HSBC with £1.24 billion.

But that's only one half of the story. The same article reveals that these same banks are expected to disclose pre-tax profits of nearly £40 billion. The mixed message is all too easy to decipher: despite record insolvencies and levels of bad debt, it still pays to lend money indiscriminately.

# Sub-Prime Party Time

*'Bankruptcy is like losing your virginity.*
*It doesn't hurt the next time.'*

Clarissa Dickson Wright, Celebrity Chef

Wednesday 14 March, 2007

**10.40 a.m. Doormat.** My official status still reads 'BANKRUPT', and yet...

*Dear Mr Livingson,*
*We all need a little extra cash now and then... but getting the money you need doesn't need to be a hassle. Give Provident a call today on* **Freephone** —— *and we could change the enclosed cheque into cash and deliver it to your home within days.*
*CASH STRAIGHT TO YOUR DOOR!*
*CCJ's? No problem – Even if you've been turned down before – Tenants and unemployed welcome.*

Looks like it's time for a spending spree. I'm brandishing a specimen cheque for £500. Should I be inclined to take up this offer, a 'local agent' will deliver the money to my door and then call round to collect the weekly payments. I've sure come a long way since the heady days of the Gold Card. Word's out amongst the lower echelons of the credit industry and I'm a (sub) prime target. Thanks but no thanks; this shit is aimed at the desperate, the stupid, or both. What kind of lunatic would take out a loan with a 177% APR?

**11.30 a.m.** Sub-prime isn't just doorstep loans, it also includes mortgages given to those with poor credit histories or risky employment status. According to a BBC report it's starting to go wrong in the US because of the amount of sub-primers defaulting. One sub-prime lender has had its shares suspended on the New York Stock Exchange. As the Chairman of the *Consumer Credit Association* once said, if people cannot pay their debts, 'it's misery for both borrower and lender'.

Thursday 22 March, 2007

**6.30 p.m. Home.** After more than a month of family hostility, relations appear to be thawing. The old man called. It was a terse exchange but a good sign nonetheless.

'I feel ashamed of you and I feel ashamed for you,' he started, clearly still vexed, 'but, whatever you've done, even if you're…' he stopped himself and breathed a heavy sigh, '…I'm still your father and you're still my son.'

And that's what it boils down to at the end of the day. Blood ties. Whatever I've done in his eyes, I am still his son. I haven't killed anyone.

We didn't stay chatting for long. I could sense he was expecting some form of apology or admission of wrongdoing. He wants me to repent in some way, but I cannot and will not betray myself. I'm glad he's coming round, I've been worrying that something terrible might happen to him while we're not speaking.

Saturday 12 May, 2007

**11.15 a.m. Doormat.** Now I really can start looking to a brighter future. A mere *five months* into my bankruptcy and I have a letter from the Official Receiver informing me that I'm being put forward for an early discharge. All I need to do is complete the enclosed 'Income and Expenditure Questionnaire', and await confirmation of my release date. In the meantime, my creditors have got 28 days to lodge any objections.

Monday 14 May, 2007

**3.30 p.m. Home.** Wasted no time and posted the questionnaire. Kelly's looking forward to it, because she can't afford to subsidise me anymore. I'll be pleased to be out of bankruptcy, but with it comes a little more reality. I've seen all of the daytime Bo-Ho's in the cafés, sitting with their scripts and their books, working on their fancy laptops and chatting with their artsy friends. How do they do it? I've asked myself this a hundred times. Are they successful already? Perhaps they're supported by rich partners? Maybe they're on the dole?

Money frees people from work, as Orwell said when he was 'down and out'. So how does a man *without* money satisfy his mundane needs? It is an art, I tell myself, an art that must be learned and practised continuously.

**Monday 4 June, 2007**
**7.30 p.m. Home.** Jan called, acting as mediator, to invite us to the grand unveiling of the new house. They're having a housewarming dinner next weekend. I'm slightly apprehensive, as it'll be the first time I'll see Dad since he waved my Bankruptcy Order at me. Maybe I could turn up wearing a black sheep costume, or perhaps tarred and feathered?

# Buying or Renting?

*'56% of respondents think that it is not fair that people who declare themselves bankrupt will be discharged in just one year, with 65% suggesting that the Bankruptcy Law should be changed to make it more difficult for a person to take this option.'*

Survey of over 1,000 Equifax customers, January 2007

Sunday 17 June, 2007

**11.45 p.m. An Englishman's Castle.** The old fella was waiting for us as our cab drew up to the new place. He was there on his own at the end of the driveway, like the lord of the manor. I was glad when he extended his hand to me as we stepped out of the car. There was a whiff of reconciliation in the air. It felt good to think we'd be able to move on.

Inside, he gave us the full tour. The house was impressive, he'd put a lot into it and I was happy that his efforts had paid off. The grand opening was a family affair, probably so I wouldn't cause any embarrassment.

'I thought about telling your mother but she'd only find a way of blaming me. I don't need the aggravation. You can tell her in your own time,' he said as his opening gambit, handing me a bottle of ale in the conservatory.

'I'm sure I will,' I said. 'In my own time.'

'So you'll be free in a few months then?'

'Yeah, how did you…'

'I've been reading up on it,' he said, revealing his parental instincts to be intact.

'I had to see what you'd let yourself in for. You'll still be blacklisted for six years and, if you do ever try and buy a place, you'll be paying through the nose for it, no bank will ever trust you again. Looks like you'll be relying on my inheritance.'

'Do you have to be so morbid?' I protested.

'The trouble with you young people is you've too much education. All this mess just proves me right: you'd have been better off leaving school and getting yourself a job.'

Later in bed, afflicted by my usual insomnia and with Kelly draped over me snoring away, I lay looking at my father's four walls. Maybe one day I would attain the holy grail of Western society and have property to my name. In a few weeks I'd be free from bankruptcy. With no debt, I could land myself a nice 50K office job and set about acquiring myself some title deeds. What a depressing thought. A society that judges non-ownership as failure is a culture not worth caring for.

### Wednesday 20 June, 2007

**10.30 a.m. Home.** Counting down the days till I'm discharged and I reach another milestone on my road to freedom. I already feel liberated. My mind and body feel cleansed and I am freer than at any other time in my life. The dark days of debt are behind me and I now sleep soundly, my slumber only disturbed by the need to get up and scrawl an urgent thought. I don't just feel unshackled from debt, I've acquired a new strength, an assuredness. I'm ready for a new phase in my life.

I know I can't hide from the realities of everyday forever, but I no longer fear its demands or the terror of a life unfulfilled. The question of how best to live is a perpetual theme, in need of constant refinement. When my hair is grey and my face lined and wrinkled, I have to be able to look in the mirror and back over the years and know I tried. When I reach that point I must be at peace, prepared for death, knowing I tried to make the best of myself and in the right way. That, surely, is all anyone can ask of themselves.

## NOTICE TO BANKRUPT ENCLOSING A SEALED COPY OF THE EARLY DISCHARGE NOTICE

### IN THE HIGH COURT OF JUSTICE

### MR P. J. LIVINGSON
### IN BANKRUPTCY

**Notice under Section 279(2) of the Insolvency Act 1986**

A bankruptcy order having been made by this court against
Mr Paul Joseph Livingson of —— LONDON,
On 4 December 2006
Pursuant to section 279(2) of the Insolvency Act 1986, the
Official Receiver states that the investigation of the bankrupt's
affairs is unnecessary or concluded.

**Notice to bankrupt**
With effect from the date that this notice is filed in court
you are discharged from bankruptcy.

## Monday 16 July, 2007

**10.45 a.m. Home.** And so it comes to an end. The investigation of my affairs is either 'unnecessary' or 'concluded' and I am no longer 'a bankrupt'. Having made full use of this country's streamlined insolvency laws, I'm free to go, after just seven months and, crucially, without the shackle of an *Income Payment Order*. I'm off the hook, content with the knowledge that none of my future toil, not one solitary bead of sweat, will go towards lining the pockets of my former money-lenders.

**11.10 a.m.** Pop! Cracked open the bottle of bubbly I've been saving for the occasion. Oh, it's a debt-free life for me…

**11.35 a.m.** I keep having to pinch myself, to remember that the events of the last few weeks really did happen. Rewind six months and I was chained to a desk in servitude to the masters of debt, engaged in joyless tasks and looking longingly out of the window dreaming of all the things I'd like to be doing. Fast forward to the present and I find myself in my dressing gown, champagne flute in hand, enjoying a pre-breakfast quaff, the only restrictions in my life being the limits of my own imagination. It's a nice place to be.

**12.00 p.m.** Significant change requires extreme acts. Seneca was right – time is our most valuable commodity. I've seized control of my days, given myself the platform I need to be able to invest in myself. It can only lead to good things. Now I'm ready to face the future and I'm full of hope.

**12.30 p.m.** It's almost time to sign off. It feels like the end of an era, a decadent period of consumerism fuelled by cheap money and a belief in everyone's inalienable right to a five-star lifestyle. It's not merely the people who are bankrupt – it's the age. Me? I'm done with this. I've been writing this diary for almost seven years now. It's time to move on. Reading through my chronicles one last time I've an urge to put it out there. Maybe someone will think it's important?

But what to call it? How to Be Bankrupt? Hello Bankruptcy? The Bankruptcy Diaries? Yes, that's what I'll call it, 'The Bankruptcy Diaries'.

And so that's what I did.